ENCYCLOPEDIA BROWN COLLECTION

by

Donald J. Sobol

SCHOLASTIC INC.
New York Toronto London Auckland Sydney
Mexico City New Delhi Hong Kong Buenos Aires

Encyclopedia Brown's Book of Strange but True Crimes,
ISBN 0-590-44148-5, copyright © 1991 by Donald J. Sobol and Rose Sobol.
Illustrations copyright © 1991 by Scholastic Inc.
Encyclopedia Brown Carries On,
ISBN 0-590-44575-8, copyright © 1982 by Donald J. Sobol.
Illustrations copyright © 1982 by Scholastic Inc.
Encyclopedia Brown Sets the Pace,
ISBN 0-590-44577-4, copyright © 1982 by Donald J. Sobol.
Illustrations copyright © 1982 by Scholastic Inc.
Encyclopedia Brown Takes the Cake!,
ISBN 0-590-44576-6, text copyright © 1982, 1983 by Donald J. Sobol.
Recipes copyright © 1982, 1983 by Glenn Andrews.
Illustrations copyright © 1983 by Scholastic Inc.

12 11 10 9 8 7 6 5 4 3 2 1   4 5 6 7 8 9/0

Printed in the U.S.A.   23

This edition created exclusively for Barnes & Noble, Inc.
2004 Barnes & Noble Books

ISBN 0-7607-6140-X

First compilation printing, November 2004

Contents

ENCYCLOPEDIA BROWN'S
BOOK OF STRANGE BUT TRUE CRIMES

Donald J. Sobol & Rose Sobol

Interior illustrations by John Zielinski

For Donna,
who brightens our lives

All the stories in this book are true, though in many cases I have changed the name and/or the location.

— D.J.S.

The Case of the
Two-Headed Toothbrush

"You know whom we haven't seen in weeks?" Encyclopedia Brown asked Sally Kimball, his junior partner in the Brown Detective Agency. "Melvin Pugh."

"I heard he's inventing a spray to make houseplants dance to a Strauss waltz," Sally said.

Melvin was always inventing something. Usually it was something nobody could use.

Two months ago, he had showed Encyclopedia his latest brainchild, a bowling ball without finger holes. It was for women who didn't want to ruin their nail polish.

"Melvin is a genius," Sally said. "He's just living on the wrong planet."

The two detectives were biking to the beach. As they turned down Fulver Street, Encyclopedia suddenly braked. "Hey, there's Melvin."

"And in trouble," Sally said.

Melvin stood on the sidewalk, surrounded by a gang of tough older boys who called themselves the Tigers. They should have called themselves the Mud Cards. They were always giving some small kid a dirty deal.

Bugs Meany, the Tigers' leader, wrinkled his nose at the sight of the two detectives. "Well, well, if it isn't the hotshot do-gooders," he taunted. "Make like Charles Lindbergh and take off."

"Encyclopedia!" Melvin cried. "Am I glad to see you! Bugs just stole my invention."

"Melvin better check his data base," Bugs growled. "The toothbrush is my invention."

Bugs held up two facing toothbrushes joined by a single handle. "With this little beauty, a person can brush the back and front of a tooth at the same time," he boasted. "It's the greatest gift to mankind since the cookie cutter with a trigger release."

"It's *my* invention, Encyclopedia," Melvin protested. "Bugs stole it from me while I was in the coin laundry down the street. Mom's washing machine broke. So I took the laundry out for her. I had the lid of the machine raised and was pushing the laundry down inside it with both hands when Bugs swiped the toothbrush from my back pocket."

"Man alive," Bugs moaned, smacking his forehead. "This kid is one heavy-duty liar! I had raised the lid on one of those machines and was pushing down my laundry with both hands. I was defense-less. So what happens? Melvin picks my back pocket and runs off with my two-headed toothbrush."

"Bugs Meany in a laundry?" Sally snapped. "Bal-oney! Since when do you wash anything?"

Bugs managed to keep his temper.

"My folks are away for the weekend," he said, winking at his Tigers. "I did my clothes in our wash-ing machine. But our dryer is broken. So I came here to use a pay machine."

"Why didn't you hang your clothes on a line to dry?" Sally inquired.

"You peasant!" Bugs exclaimed. "Clothes hanging in the Meany backyard? Have you no refinement, no breeding?"

"Let's walk back to the coin laundry," Encyclo-pedia said. "I want to see your wet clothes, Bugs."

"Too late," Bugs said. "After Melvin stole my toothbrush, I had Spike Larson, my right-hand man, take the clothes to my house. That coin laundry isn't safe for honest citizens."

Encyclopedia nodded thoughtfully. Spike Larson wasn't in the group of Tigers.

"There has to be a witness," Sally said. "Someone in the laundry must have seen what happened."

"There weren't any other customers," Melvin muttered glumly.

"What about the person who runs the laundry?" Sally asked.

"As I came in, the phone rang and she went into the office to answer it," Melvin said. "The laundry was empty when Bugs stole my toothbrush."

"When you stole *my* toothbrush," Bugs insisted. "Now run along, Melvin, and invent something of your own. Wait, I've got it! Make it round and call it a wheel!"

The other Tigers howled with glee and joined in.

"Invent a shaving cream for boys under six. Have it smell like crayons."

"How about a stupid computer you can beat at checkers!"

"A self-cleaning bathtub!"

"Motorized garbage cans!"

"A swimming pool table!"

"Retread sneakers!"

At each suggestion, the Tigers rocked with laughter. Melvin looked ready to break into tears.

Sally shouted for the heckling to stop. Fists clenched, she marched up to Bugs. "I ought to knock the truth out of you, you pimplehead!"

Sally wasn't bluffing. She was the only kid in elementary school who dared to trade punches with the Tigers' leader. After taking one of her famous uppercuts, Bugs would wobble around like a drunk in an earthquake. Then he'd pitch to the ground and lie there till it was safe to get up.

"Back off," Bugs warned Sally. "I never went all out with you. But start something now, and I'll for-

4

get I'm a mother's dream. I'll fold you up like a pocketknife."

The other Tigers edged close to Sally.

Encyclopedia saw it was time to step in.

"You stole the two-headed toothbrush, Bugs," he said. "You've been lying."

"Oh, yeah?" Bugs retorted. "Prove it!"

"Allow me," Encyclopedia said politely.

He whispered into Bugs's ear.

Bugs blinked. Bugs reddened. Bugs looked as if he'd swallowed a bag of prunes.

"You know I was only fooling around," he mumbled weakly.

He handed Encyclopedia the toothbrush and tried to save face.

"Heck, I wouldn't want anyone thinking I really invented something this dumb," he jeered as he led his Tigers away.

Melvin hopped with joy. "The toothbrush will be bigger than my ladies' bowling ball. And I have you to thank, Encyclopedia. You ought to write a book."

"I'm collecting material," Encyclopedia said. "I've got a whole scrapbook filled with wacky true crimes."

"Let me see it!" Melvin begged.

"Come on over this evening," Encyclopedia invited.

The Browns had just finished dinner when Melvin rang the doorbell. Encyclopedia led him into the garage. From a shelf on the rear wall, the detective took down a large scrapbook.

"Here," he said to Melvin.

Melvin turned eagerly to the first page. He began to read. . . .

For the solution to The Case of the Two-Headed Toothbrush, turn to page 112.

1.
Wacky Crimes

"**I don't.**" Mauro Pirelli of Vicenza, Italy, was a jittery bridegroom.

Two hours before his wedding he had his hair cut. While seated in the barber's chair, he anxiously considered his future as a husband.

As his doubts worsened, inspiration struck.

He borrowed a car, sped to nearby Thiene, and climbed into a second-story window.

He clumped and clattered to make sure the homeowner heard him. Then he left a trail even a blind detective couldn't miss.

The police arrived in the nick of time — as Pirelli was going into the church to be married.

"I attempted a robbery just to get arrested and avoid the wedding," Pirelli confessed at his trial.

A panel of judges found him guilty of attempted robbery but withheld a prison sentence.

He's alive and kicking, isn't he?   The law finally caught up with Cristina Echvarria, a lady of many addresses. Among her offenses: practicing medicine without a license, and billing Medicaid for treating a 220-pound football player for diaper rash.

It's the reel thing.   A thief in Canton, China, suffered from catching a cola.

Yup, a cola, not a cold.

Guards at the Chrysanthemum Guest House nabbed him as he sipped a soda he had just reeled in.

Police identified him as the celebrated "fishing burglar." He specialized in pulling valuables through hotel windows with a fishing rod.

The layered look.   Two Senegalese crooks learned clothes don't always make the man. Sometimes they make the prisoner.

The pair broke into a clothing shop in Paris and waddled out with lots of stylish threads. The cops quickly spotted them. The two men were dressed in a total of fourteen leather vests, three jackets, one coat, and six pairs of trousers.

Trial by file.   For two years Astred Greene flew the world free, saving herself an estimated $40,000 in air fares. She masqueraded as a flight attendant.

Greene got aboard overseas flights by walking past the gate agent, who took her for a member of the crew.

One mistake did her in. She was too good at the job. Passengers wrote letters to the airline praising her helpfulness.

An office worker decided to start putting the letters in Greene's personnel file. Whoops, no file.

Unforgettable 1. "All I can remember about him is, he was stark naked," said Anne Barkley of Tampa, Florida, when asked to describe the man who stole her purse.

Unforgettable 2. "Well, he had big eyes," said Ellie Ford of Charleston, South Carolina, when asked to describe the Peeping Tom she saw at her window.

Join the dinar's club. In 1987, five tourists from West Germany were arrested for lighting their cigarettes with 100-dinar bills in the Koral Hotel in Umag, Yugoslavia.

One of the tourists took pictures of the lighting for laughs. A hotel employee became so angered that he called the police. The film was held for evidence.

A judge fined the tourists the equivalent of $30 each and denied them all "Yugoslav hospitality" (that is, the freedom to visit the country) for three years.

A 100-dinar note was worth about 15 cents.

Cash and carry. Two women selected $419 worth of clothes in a department store in Heath, Ohio. They paid with a fake $1,000 bill.

The bill bore the phrases "A. Phony-bill" and "U. Cantcashit."

The store couldnotcashit. It was too large a bill. So a clerk took one of the women to a neighboring store.

No one there noticed anything unusual either, and the two women walked off with their new clothes and $581 in real-money change.

All wet. Boyd Cross of Fort Lauderdale, Florida, came home from work to eat lunch and found a burglar in his bedroom.

Cross grabbed a gun, which he kept for protection. In the struggle with the burglar, the gun went off, wounding Cross's waterbed and flooding the house.

The burglar sprinted away with nothing except wet feet.

Look away, look away. As part of a class project, three high school students got the okay from the manager of a Chicago department store to shoplift goods in full view of customers.

The students made out like bandits.

"They must have taken at least four hundred dollars' worth of merchandise," said their teacher.

During the three hours the students played their roles, there were more than 100 customers in the store. At least half saw the "shoplifting." The students got one dirty·look. The rest of the customers either looked away or walked away.

"I'm totally amazed," their teacher said. "I thought maybe fifteen percent would report them. The indifference underscores what we're seeing more and more — a society that doesn't want to get involved."

Hold 'em, roll.   Mrs. Tillie Tangleber's restaurant in New York City served hard rolls. Hard as in *haarrrd*.

Early on a winter night Alexander Godwin, a barber, sat down at a table by the window facing the street. He ordered a cup of coffee and one of those hard rolls.

He had buttered the roll and was raising it to his mouth when things went crazy. A stranger stepped close to the window, whipped out a gun, and fired.

Godwin didn't have time to duck, and didn't have to. He had the roll.

The bullet splintered the window and struck the roll, which snuffed its force to a driblet. Deadened instead of deadly, the bullet dropped into Godwin's mouth, wounding him barely enough to draw blood.

The stranger apparently mistook Godwin for someone else and was never seen again.

All are not hunters who blow the horn. A Crime Stoppers TV program in Florida reenacted unsolved crimes with the hope that viewers who had information would tell the police.

Realism was the watchword. In one of the shows, a detective played the role of the robber of a milk store. A female rookie played his partner in crime.

Two weeks later a woman walked into police headquarters and surrendered. "You've got me red-handed," she said. She thought the reenactment of the holdup was a film taken while the actual crime was being committed.

Kiss and wow! Umberto Rizzo was a World War II airman when he kissed his sweetheart on a street corner in Messina, Sicily.

A policeman with no sense of romance reported his conduct.

Rizzo married the young woman, but it didn't help. He received a suspended three-month sentence for "indecency in a public place."

Forty years later the Italian Treasury Ministry decided that the sentence eliminated Rizzo, now 69, from a veterans' pension.

Moreover, the Ministry demanded back the $8,500 already paid him.

Hidden assets. In 1937, Joseph Mancini, a New York City druggist, saved $6,700 because he always wore long underwear, winter and summer.

Mancini had just sold his house for $68,000, and was carrying the $6,700 cash deposit. As he and his attorney entered a cab, two men shoved in behind them.

The attorney managed to jump as the cab slowed for a corner. The thieves jumped, too, with Mancini's pants.

Mancini told police that he had hidden the $6,700 in the leg of his underwear. The thieves got only the $15 in his pants.

Know a woman by the companies she keeps. Dumbest Victims of the Year award for 1912 went to the Hoboken, New Jersey, merchants who paid a smartly dressed woman for goods she stole from them.

Maisie B. Copeland was a wholesale shoplifter. After a few days, she would return the merchandise and coolly demand a refund in cash.

The merchants made good though they were somewhat puzzled. She had no sales slips, and they had no record of the sales.

Copeland swindled thousands of dollars before store owners began swapping notes on a lady customer they never could satisfy.

She was taken to the Central Police Station, where, like a lady of quality, she promptly swooned to the floor.

Sad but true. In 1930, the villagers of Zude, Poland, were convicted of stealing a forest.

The women did not appear in court, but the village's 68 men did. They said they cut down the nearby municipal forest to use as fuel. Otherwise, they would have frozen during the winter.

The judge fined them and sentenced them to brief terms in jail. He warned them not to steal any more trees.

"Your honor," one villager replied. "That is impossible. I myself took home the last tree within miles and burned it."

Time on his paws. A watch salesman in a shop in Shanxi, China, was being *watched* by police.

He had become the prime suspect when watches began disappearing left and right.

Just before police pounced, another salesman moved the watch counter.

Underneath was the real thief — a rat dwelling in a hole shining with 27 watches.

It wooden work. Nevin Curtis had stopped for a red light in downtown Cincinnati, Ohio, when two thugs jerked open his car door. One of them seized him by the leg and tried to drag him out.

Curtis stomped on the gas and whizzed off. The shocked pair were left in a blast of exhaust — holding Curtis's artificial leg.

Although the leg cost Curtis $1,625, its resale value was small. It was made to his measure.

'Hose guilty? Alfred Higgs of Portland, Oregon, said a nagging wife drove him to a life of crime.

After nine years of marriage, Higgs had had enough of her henpecking. He reached for a hose.

Oh, no, he didn't beat his wife. He unscrewed the nozzle and held up three stores at nozzlepoint.

"It was a spur of the moment thing," Higgs told

the judge. "I had been nagged so much by my wife about getting money, so I tried it."

Bridge, anyone? "Good thing the road is tied down," said a police spokesman after someone stole a 20-foot timber bridge that spanned a canal near Bunnell, Florida.

Sleeper. Two men with clubs forced their way into the apartment of Juan Sanchez.

Sanchez, who lived in a public housing project in Hato Rey, Puerto Rico, told the thieves he had nothing of any real value.

Unwilling to leave empty-handed, they took apart Sanchez's bed, loaded it on top of their car, and drove away.

Can do. Manfred Dreschler collected nickels, bottle by bottle and can by can.

He stole more than 60,000 empty, used bottles and cans from a warehouse in Geneva, New York. By turning them in at a redemption center, he collected the five-cent deposit on each and every one.

Investigators estimated that between 1980 and 1982 his piggy bank took in as much as $21,000. The sum represents about 400,000 bottles and cans.

Doze weren't hepatitis shots. A man who claimed to be a public health official telephoned the post

17

office in Kaohsiung, Taiwan. He said a doctor was coming to vaccinate the employees against type-B hepatitis, a disease sweeping the area.

The "doctor" arrived in a hospital uniform. He told the seven employees that the shots might cause a brief spell of sleepiness. Hadn't they better close the post office for a few minutes?

The employees did as he advised and dozed off. When they woke up one and a half hours later, the "doctor" and all the cash — $5,526 — were gone.

Sympathetic response.   An English hospital loaned teddy bears to small children during their stay. The stuffed animals made too big a hit. They were smuggled home at a rate of ten a month.

The nurses halted the practice by putting bandages on the bears. The children thought they were sick and needed to be kept in the hospital.

Prime time.   Japanese police arrested Saburo Yoshida for making 1,400 long-distance telephone calls to Prime Minister Yasuhiro Nakasone's private office.

Yoshida called from a pay phone in Innoshima, 400 miles west of Tokyo, up to 100 times a day over a period of four months.

The calls lasted about three seconds because Yoshida could afford to deposit only one ten-yen (four cents) coin. He never spoke.

"My salary is low," explained Yoshida, a high school English teacher. "And I don't have any friends. Anyway, I thought I'd call the Prime Minister and annoy him."

Skimming the cream. Thieves pried off the lid of the safe in the Tinee Giant Market in Portsmouth, Virginia. The opening, alas, was too small for them to reach in and grab the money.

Their solution to the problem was all wet.

They dumped ten gallons of milk into the safe. The paper money floated within easy reach.

You can't see the doctor without an appointment. A burglar mistakenly sawed his way into Dr. Harley Kojak's office in Durham, North Carolina, and apologized in a note left on the doctor's desk.

"Sorry, wrong building, Doc."

Nothing, not even an aspirin, was missing.

Stepping stones. Harlan Orlando stole 175 diamonds worth $550,000 from a Nashville jewelry store. He hid them in a pair of old shoes, which he left with his father while he went on a fishing trip.

In his absence, his father gave some old clothing, including the shoes, to a child care center. The children played with the jewels for a week without knowing they were real.

Then Orlando appeared at the center. He demanded the jewels back so furiously that a teacher became suspicious. She called police.

Now, please, don't sit there mumbling, "If the shoe fits, wear it."

He wasn't trying to stiff them.   Dr. Daniel Hunter was instructing a class of arthritis patients in Norfolk, Virginia.

One exercise called for the oldsters to raise their hands in the air.

"Stick 'em up!" Hunter hollered.

At that moment a passerby chanced to look through the window. Horrified, he telephoned the cops.

Police cars, sirens wailing, closed in on the building.

Hunter explained that the "stickup" was for the victims' health, not their money.

Purse snatching — take two. A pedestrian in Knoxville, Tennessee, saw a hoodlum snatch a woman's purse. He gave chase, tackled the crook, and held him for police — who arrived with surprising speed.

The problem was, the crook was a police officer. The purse-snatching was being staged for a local television station.

The crimestopper left the scene before anyone learned his name.

"I think he went away mad," said a police lieu-tenant. "I'd like to know who he was so we could write a letter praising him. He did exactly what I wish everyone would do."

Hopping mad.   Someone got off on the wrong foot by stealing 300 sneakers from a shoe salesman's station wagon in Columbia, South Carolina.

There wasn't a matching pair of sneakers in the lot.

Shoe salesmen usually have signs on their cars stating:

THESE SHOES ARE FOR ONE FOOT ONLY
PLEASE DON'T STEAL

The robbed station wagon was signless.

Expect to be treated as you treat others.   In a double take, Gilberto Mennes of Ponce, Puerto Rico, snatched the wallet of the mugger who had snatched his.

"It was sticking out of his back pocket," said Mennes. "I didn't have time to think. I just grabbed it. He never looked back."

Mennes's wallet contained only identification papers.

The mugger's wallet had a driver's license and $33, which he got back after his arrest.

It might have been worse.   Three thieves took almost everything valuable from 50 guests at a wedding party in Bergamo, Italy. The softies let the bride keep her wedding ring.

He struck oil.   After two flags were stolen from the post office in Oshkosh, Wisconsin, the postmaster had the 20-foot pole greased. The Stars and Stripes went up and down, but not the thief.

One for the books.   Police searching the home of a Wisconsin man found more than 4,000 public library books "borrowed" over the past 20 years.

And the dog's name is Buck.   A visitor to Davenport, Iowa, told police that he had been robbed of $300 by a "big, friendly dog" obviously trained to lift wallets.

What a gas.   A robber hit a Tulsa service station eight times in the same year. Practice made him close to perfect. He shaved his holdup time to 30 seconds.

All that glitters is not gold.   The old proverb was learned afresh by a gang of thieves who robbed the Tse Sui Luen Jewelry Store in Hong Kong.
   The nine gold bars they stole from a show window

were fake, worth about $800 instead of the expected $108,000.

The disgusted gang dumped the bars in a restaurant men's room along with a note addressed to the jewelry store manager. The note bitterly complained that he was cheating his customers.

The manager denied the charge. "It is normal practice to display fake gold bars in the store's windows for safety reasons," he said.

The thieves did get away with $42,000 in jewelry.

Birdbrain! Acting on a tip, Dallas police found hundreds of dollars' worth of stolen merchandise in the lodging of a 19-year-old youth on probation.

A parrot in the room greeted the officers with "Hello, Cindy. Hello, Jack." The youth insisted he'd bought the bird from a man known to him only as Shorty.

Police checked through reports of stolen parrots. They found that a parrot named Jack, valued at $2,800, had been stolen from Cindy Mathesson, owner of a card shop.

Mathesson was summoned to the police station. At the sight of her, the parrot flapped its wings excitedly and screaked, "Cindy!"

"Jack!" she cried back.

The youth pleaded guilty to theft and was sentenced to three years in prison.

"The moral of this story," said an assistant district attorney, "is that if you steal a talking parrot, you'd better retrain him."

Soap story. Trudy Case of Walla Walla, Washington, came home to find her front door forced open.

The only thing the intruder had taken was a bath.

"Maybe we'll have to round up housebreakers who normally are dirty and now are suddenly clean," remarked a police officer.

One for the road. On a Monday morning Allen Statler opened his auto repair shop in Des Moines and thought something looked different. Over the weekend, thieves had hauled away 25 feet of sidewalk in front of his business, brick by brick.

Seventy-six would be the spirit. Skateboarder Mitch Collins, 19, was pulled over for speeding on the downhill of a California interstate highway and told he was doing 72 miles an hour.

"That simply isn't true," said Collins. "I was doing seventy-five!"

He had it maid. An unidentified "victim" in Gilroy, California, returned home to find it had been cleaned out.

Correction: cleaned *up*.

Someone had gathered the dirty laundry, made

the bed, washed the dishes, and hung new drapes.

The volunteer housekeeper left a note:

> Dear Sir,
> I hope you don't mind. I cleaned your
> house. Don't worry. I didn't take anything
> because my father is a Duke in Spain. I'll
> clean your house for as long as you live
> here.
>
> Prince Eddie.

"We're not sure what we could charge him with," said the local police commander. "It's too bad he didn't break into my house."

Overtime. How many employees break into a business to go to work?

The owner of a fast-food restaurant in Memphis declared bankruptcy. That night he had all the locks on the building changed.

The next morning four employees showed up at the regular opening time. They smashed the drive-in window, crawled inside, got the deep fryer and the soda machine going, and began serving takeout orders.

It was business as usual — until the owner drove by.

The foursome had pocketed $398 before the police shut them down.

Purse snacker. Officials at a zoo in Arnhem, Holland, put up signs warning visitors to guard their handbags.

Not only did the thief make the zoo her home, she had a marvelously long reach, and she was beyond the law.

Her name was Quimba. She was rather attractive if you like them big. However, she wasn't the type heroes chase after.

An elephant, Quimba used her trunk to pluck the handbags, which she swallowed with a satisfied *glub*.

Paper chase. Thieves hit a stationery company in Coventry, England, seven times in less than a year and walked off with everything they could lift.

As if figuring it would be an even easier place to loot without a security system, they sneaked back and stole the burglar alarm.

"They probably needed the alarm to protect the eighteen thousand dollars' worth of stuff they stole from us," said a company spokesman.

Thanks, we needed that. Fifteen Democratic committeemen were gathered in Denver to assign subjects for the state platform in the November election.

"Who's going to take crime?" asked the chairman of the resolutions committee. No one answered.

He repeated the question twice, but got no takers.

Finally he said, "Someone has to take crime."

At that, three men charged into the room, took everyone's money, and charged out.

It's not what you say, it's how you say it. In Rochester, New York, Janice Manton was seen leaving a jewelry store holdup where nine rings had been stolen at gunpoint.

She was overtaken driving to Henrietta. Police searched the car, uncovered a gun, but no rings. They tried to question her.

She replied by pressing her lips together.

Finally, she mumbled that she wanted to see her lawyer.

Mumbling was her goof.

Police found the nine rings in her mouth.

Desert raiders.   In Arizona cactus rustling became so common that the plant had to be protected by law.

Yet the thievery continues. In one case, a 19-foot saguaro cactus was stolen in Quartzite. Wanted posters of the plant were nailed up along the state border.

A tipster spotted the cactus on sale in a Nevada nursery for $15,000. The elderly couple from whom it was stolen picked it out of a police lineup. The thieves were then caught and convicted.

Try it, you'll like it.　A gang in India had thievery down to a tea.

The gang mingled with regular tea sellers on the platform of the Kalyan railroad station and sold passengers tea laced with knockout drops.

As the train pulled out, members of the gang climbed aboard. As soon as their victims fell asleep, they relieved them of their cash and valuables and hopped off at the next stop.

Bedside manner.　An undertaker in Kuala Lampur, Malaysia, was fined the equivalent of $12 for entering a hospital without permission and selling coffins to the patients.

2.
Dumbo Desperados

No way out. In Coventry, England, a clothing store burglar seeking a fast getaway went bananas running into one fake exit after another. All led to a brick wall.

After trying 12 dummy doors, which were background scenery for a fashion display, he climbed a staircase, lost his footing, and knocked himself out.

Doughnut unto others. In Frankfort, Kentucky, a Brinks guard carried a bag of money from a supermarket and put it in his armored truck. Feeling hunger pangs, he went back and bought a bag of doughnuts.

As he approached his truck, two armed thugs knocked him down. The birdbrains grabbed the bag of doughnuts and, believing themselves rich, escaped by car.

Money to burn.   A gang of safecrackers called itself the Japanese Ninja, after the Japanese assassins of feudal days.

The Ninjas operated in California in the 1980s with burning failure. In three robberies in a row, they used blowtorches to open safes, frying to ashes the money inside.

Role playing.   Time caught up with a pair of house burglars in São Paulo, Brazil.

They were so old that one burglar, Pedro de

Rosas, 74, couldn't hear his partner, Juan Alves, 73, scream that the police were coming.

"They should have known better," said police inspector Osvaldo da Silva. "I think they wanted to relive the good old days. But Alves, who doesn't hear well, was still busy stealing when we arrived."

De Rosas made an effort to run for it, but his varicose veins held him to a fast shuffle.

Photo finish. It wasn't so much the crudeness of the phony bank notes that irked the judge in Nairobi, Kenya. It was the picture.

The counterfeiter, Whythe Ngugi, said he saw nothing wrong with printing his own picture on the 100-shilling note, worth $7.70. His bearded portrait replaced that of President Moi in the center of the bill.

The self-centered Ngugi pondered the high price of vanity behind bars.

Doesn't everyone save receipts? Harry Lyle picked up a hitchhiker outside Bismarck, North Dakota. The hitchhiker drew a gun, took $60 from Lyle, and asked for a *receipt*. When the police tracked him down, he still had the receipt in his pocket.

That's the way the ice floes. On a freezing day in January, three girls, all 16 years old, mugged a woman on the northern tip of Manhattan Island.

They took her purse and chose a tricky escape route along the ice-clogged shore.

All at once they found themselves drifting away on a hunk of ice about six feet square. They floated north on the Hudson River for an hour until rescued by a police helicopter.

"They didn't say much of anything," said the pilot, Robert Hegel. "They were glad to get off even if it meant getting locked up."

Are you sure Houdini started this way? A 16-year-old in New Haven, Connecticut, attempted to force his way into a house and became stuck in the window grating.

He had removed two bolts from the bars around

a first-floor window and had started crawling through. One of the bars snapped back and trapped him. Halfway in and halfway out, he managed to reach the telephone and called 911, the emergency number. He asked if someone would please come and rescue him.

As he was led away by the police, he muttered, "I'm embarrassed. This is my first burglary."

Weight-watchers. Food was steadily disappearing from a warehouse in Prague, Czechoslovakia. After $120,000 worth of munchies had vanished, suspicion centered on the warehouse supervisor. He had ballooned to 506 pounds.

The judge put him on a 12-year diet of prison chow.

High flier. Cat burglar Garvey Forman plied his craft at a theatrical boardinghouse in Chicago. In the course of his search for goodies, he tiptoed into the room of a sturdy six-footer, Mrs. Beatrice Renn.

Renn shrilled the alarm and applied a numbing headlock. With the last of his strength, Forman wrenched free and wobbled into the hall. He was greeted by members of a circus troupe.

Hyman Reinke, the strongman, seized him and caused him to perform a brilliant series of contortions. Others joined in the fun.

Forman escaped by accomplishing a passable version of a big-top act, the "flying leap for life," down a flight of stairs. Pursued by the circus troupe, he dashed along Halsted Street and flung himself into the safety of a policeman's arms.

They threw the book at them.   In Camden, New Jersey, a couple had a gun, but Bonnie and Clyde they weren't.

They tried to hold up a *library*.

An assistant librarian convinced them the library had only a few coins in overdue book fines.

"Looks like we picked the wrong place to rob," the woman grumped to her companion.

Thirty minutes later they were arrested reading magazines in front of the library.

Long shot.   A gambler from Dayton, Ohio, waltzed blithely up to the cashier's window at a Las Vegas casino and asked for $7,500 in chips.

The cashier immediately became suspicious. The gambler's cash was in bank wrappers and stuffed in a bank bag.

The gambler lost his stake — the loot from a bank holdup — before he could make a bet.

Okay, okay, how about a pretzel?   A masked man waved a kitchen knife at a clerk in a liquor store in Jackson, Mississippi, and angrily demanded money.

The clerk responded by smacking a metal pipe on the counter.

Shaken, the masked man blurted, "Just give me twenty dollars."

The clerk glared silently.

"Can I take a bag of potato chips?"

When the clerk shook his head, the masked man skedaddled.

Bad training. A motorman in New York City stopped his subway train and took $11 from a drunk sleeping on a platform. He chose the wrong victim. The drunk was a police decoy.

Name brand. Sheila Townsend of Duluth, Minnesota, pleaded not guilty to breaking into a car and stealing clothing and other property. The attire she wore to court, a sports warm-up outfit, said otherwise.

"Those are my clothes!" gasped the victim, Mrs. Ida Kearns. "My name is inside."

It sure was, on the collar. Townsend changed her plea to guilty.

A mansion is a *big* house. A midnight burglar slipped through the window of a mansion in Scarsdale, New York, and became lost. He did find a bedroom, shook owner Jason Frankenthal awake, and asked the way out.

Frankenthal ushered him to the front door. Then he described the confused burglar to the police, who made the arrest before dawn.

Help needed — and how.   Two harebrained hoods entered a U-Totem convenience store in Cleveland and requested job application forms.

They filled out the forms, left the store, and returned with a gun.

They didn't get much opportunity to spend their $380 take. The boneheads had left their job applications forms, filled out with their names and addresses, in the store.

Catchy little number.   A young man tried to telephone his father in Shreveport after breaking into a city building in New Orelans.

Instead of dialing "9" to make an outside call, his finger slipped and he dialed "0." That connected him with police dispatchers. He was still holding the telephone when officers came for him.

He shot the works.   Tony Mercir broke into a city building in Pittsburgh. He found a Polaroid camera in one of the offices and took his own picture. When it came out black, he tossed it into a trash basket.

"He didn't understand how the camera works," said one officer. "It takes a little time for the picture to develop."

Now think hard. When was the last time you saw a thief take his own picture at the scene of the crime and leave it there?

Armed with a copy of the photo, a police officer spotted Mercir, a picture of innocence, in downtown Pittsburgh. He was snapped again — with handcuffs.

True grit. In Philadelphia, Janice Fullwood, a barmaid, had a splitting headache. A thug made it worse. He put a pistol to her temple.

"Open the cash register and pass me the money," he ordered.

Instead of jumping to obey, she snapped, "I'm sick. Get it yourself."

The gunman hesitated, looked around, and decided to leave.

"I wasn't scared," said Fullwood. "I was just sick, and I wasn't moving for anybody."

How's buy you? Two teenagers stopped at a rare coin and stamp gallery in Montgomery, Alabama. They had some 17th-century coins to sell.

Owner Mason Stadler recognized the coins, which he kept in his home. He also noticed one of the youths was wearing his niece's gold charm bracelet and his wife's necklaces.

Mason told the teenagers to have a seat. His 230-

pound, 6-foot-3-inch security guard kept his eye on the thieves until police arrived.

The coins and jewelry had been stolen from Stadler's home three hours earlier, along with a shotgun, a battery-operated television, and a portable radio.

"Of all the houses in the city to burglarize," said Sergeant Bill Atwater, "they break into his house and turn around and try to sell the stuff back to him. They were dumbfounded that this could possibly happen. They couldn't believe it."

Clean living. Stockholm, Sweden, had a "wash-and-wear" thief. He would shed his dirty duds, bathe, and put on the clothes of the homeowner, before slipping out with guns, cameras, and jewelry. He flubbed, finally. He left his name and address in the clothes he tossed to the floor.

Underwhere? Sean Starr pleaded guilty to shoplifting in a pet shop in northern England. An employee grew suspicious of his odd walk as he headed for the door. Police found a pair of four-foot pythons stuffed in his underwear.

Which way to the recruiting office, sergeant? Three bumbling bandits invaded a house they thought belonged to a drug dealer in Miami, Florida.

It didn't. It belonged to a fireman, Louis Johnson, and his wife, Barbara.

Two of the bandits, Ed Mullins and Arthur Lopes, tied up the couple. The third, Alfred Fowler, held a gun on the Johnsons to show he meant business. The bullets fell out.

Next they snipped the cord of a can opener, thinking it was a telephone line, and ransacked the house.

The only drugs they found were pills Johnson took for a heart condition. They settled for cash, jewelry, liquor, and clothing. The most valuable item, Mrs. Johnson's ring, they dropped in the garage as they raced for their car.

The best was saved for last.

Speeding away, the champs overshot their turn, thought a guardhouse was a tollbooth, and whizzed into the Homestead Air Force base.

The military police let them call a lawyer.

You're only as good as your tools. A man stood at the counter of a convenience store in Lansing, Michigan, and asked for a pack of cigarettes. He reached into his pocket as if reaching for money and produced a revolver.

"Don't move!" he bawled.

Whereupon something did — the barrel of his gun. It fell off.

"Never mind," he said to the clerk, picked up the barrel, and beat a hasty retreat.

Sorry, the number you have reached is in working order. An anonymous caller made Dan Barkley an offer he couldn't refuse.

The caller had stolen jewelry, rings, and diamonds to sell. But he had dialed the wrong number. Oh, boy, did he ever! Barkley was a New York City police captain.

Don't get around much anymore. Steven Corey of Detroit taped a shotgun to his leg. While walking toward a drugstore he was planning to rob, he shot and wounded himself.

Short fuse, long walk. If you're going to be a robber, it doesn't pay to lose your temper.

In St. Louis a man drove up to a gas station, approached the attendant, and demanded money. The attendant told him all the cash was locked up in a safe.

The would-be robber stomped off in a rage, forgetting his car.

The next morning came the reminder. License plate numbers aren't fingerprints, but tag you they can.

Leave the driving to us. Six months after jumping bail on a disorderly conduct charge in central New York, Charles Hanson was hitchhiking to New York City. A car with two men stopped for him. As he

41

climbed into the backseat, one of the men turned around and said, "Charlie, you're under arrest again."

The man was the officer who had made the original arrest.

Bud wiser. "After the mistakes I've made, I don't think I have any political future whatsoever." The speaker, a 20-year-old freshman state senator, had just been convicted of stealing two cases of beer from a food store.

Good-bye, two shoes. Paul Caruso broke into a home in Mt. Kisco, New York. He took off his sneakers and stuffed his wallet with his birth certificate and a picture of himself (wearing the sneakers) into a sneaker. Surprised by the homeowner, Caruso fled, leaving behind the sneakers and wallet. He did ten years without them.

Slick trick. Two dumbdumbs bought a can of motor oil in a convenience store in Davie, Florida. They put the can into a paper bag.

Then they held up the clerk and put the cash into a second paper bag.

Grinning with success, they hustled out with one of the bags — the one with the motor oil.

"Why in the world these guys were not able to keep straight which bag the money was in is beyond me," said a detective. "But then, we're not dealing with brain surgeons."

Party crashers. A West German youth passed stolen goods out the window of a house in Frankfurt and straight into the hands of police.

The police had come to the scene to investigate a suspicious noise. At the sight of the law, the youth's two good buddies fled.

"Here . . . take this cassette player," the young burglar said. "Now give me the crowbar. There's a lot more."

The police cooperated until they had collected all the evidence they needed.

Say jeez! In Rome, Italy, a couple of hoodlums riding motorscooters forced themselves into the picture. Two women tourists from Japan were posing for a friend when the hoodlums roared up, bowled them over, and roared off with their jewelry and purses.

The friend kept clicking his camera. Police used the mug shots to make the arrest.

Shop at home. A burglar looting the home of Murray Resnick of Savannah was surprised in the act. Waving a handgun, he herded Resnick, his wife, and three children into a bedroom.

Resnick stayed cool. He admired the burglar's gun and offered to buy it.

The burglar said he wanted $40 and not a penny less.

Resnick wrote out a personal check to cash. The burglar grabbed it, handed over the gun, and raced away.

Nickled and dimed. Back in 1915, some fast-working burglars moved a heavy safe from its position under an electric light in the Woolworth five-and-dime store in Camden, New Jersey. In its place they substituted a safe made of cardboard. The crudely constructed mock-up was good enough to fool the night watchman on his rounds.

The burglars had pushed the store's "burglar-proof" safe into a dark corner. After the watchman passed, they forced the door open. The only hitch in the operation was the money inside, less than $100.

Bag man. Albert McDennis of New York City was walking his dog. Abiding by the city's cleanup law, he had carefully put the waste into a paper bag when a burly man came up and snarled, "Give me what you got there."

McDennis handed over the bag without delay.

Said McDennis, "He must be New York's dumbest mugger."

What a pill. The burglar had a bad case of nerves. He kept threatening Cara Phillips as he ransacked her St. Paul home.

The strain took its toll. He complained of head pains and asked for some aspirin.

Phillips handed him Valium tablets from her bedside table. He gulped them down.

When he was slumbering like a bear, she telephoned police.

Don't call us, we'll call you. Three dimwits in Peterborough, England, kidnapped Federigo Dante, an Italian baker.

They telephoned his home and demanded $7,500 in ransom. A family member asked for more time to raise the money.

The kidnappers agreed to the delay.

"We won't call again," one of them said. "When you have the money, ring us."

He helpfully supplied a telephone number.

Guess what happened next.

Ask a foolish question. A gent with zero brainpower asked a policeman in Athens, Georgia, to find out if he was wanted anywhere.

A computer answered that he was — for a holdup in his hometown of Tuckahoe, New York, two years before.

The FBI brought him home.

It's getting harder to make a dishonest buck. In Little Rock, Arkansas, a dingbat entered a jewelry store and took the routine out of the clerk's day.

"This is a stickup," he announced.

He fumbled through his pockets, frowned, and grumbled, "I forgot my gun. I'll be right back."

When he returned a few minutes later, the clerk said she didn't have the money ready for him.

She did have a cop.

Now *that's* acting. An unemployed actor attempted to hold up a San Diego restaurant with a hairbrush and was convicted of armed assault.

3.
Honest to Goodness

Capitol idea.   A small glass paperweight was sent to Governor Anthony S. Earl of Wisconsin 20 years after it had been snitched.

A woman confessed that her son had taken it during a class visit to the capitol.

She wrote the governor:

> *I've always thought we should send it back where it belonged, but we never did until this morning. Please forgive my son for taking it, and also me for not insisting that he send it right back.*

Welcome to the fold.   A man in his 80's rang Mason Haines's doorbell in Louisville, Kentucky.

The elderly stranger offered to return Haines's wallet. But first Haines had to sign a note promising not to have him arrested.

"I signed but couldn't believe what was happening," Haines said. "He wouldn't permit any questions and gave no explanation. He just took the paper and left."

The wallet had vanished, had been mislaid or was lifted, 40 years ago. Everything was there — cash, Social Security card, draft registration, and family pictures.

The light touch. After stringing up her Christmas lights, Betsy Hoffa of Phoenix, Arizona, laid a note on her porch for the thieves who had ripped off her two dozen bulbs the previous year.

The note read:

> *I think that having all the lights stolen last year was enough. There are children living here who would like to enjoy Christmas. We're trying to celebrate the birth of our Savior, not thieves.*

The following night she found the stolen bulbs on her doorstep along with a note written in a child's script:

> *We're sorry, we were only borrowing the lights. We replaced the broken one. Merry Christmas to you and your kids.*

Commented Mrs. Hoffa, "Thank goodness for honest thieves."

An old clipping. "Are you Eddie?" a gray-haired man said anxiously to Eddie Fenton, owner of a barbershop in Chicago.

Fenton, busy with a customer, nodded.

The man laid an envelope on the counter and said, "This is yours." On his way out, he added, "I'll be back for a haircut."

In the envelope was $125 stolen from Fenton 17 years before.

Boo! The week before Halloween, Sandy Halotte of Concord, New Hampshire, heard a noise on her porch during the night. The next morning her two daughters, aged 5 and 8, tearfully reported their pumpkin was gone.

For a day the thief apparently tussled with the memory of how he had felt when *his* pumpkin was stolen. The memory won.

He returned the Halottes' pumpkin with the note:

Sorry, I forgot. It happened to me when I was 3, and I cried my brains out. I'm really sorry.
                                    The Night Man.

Don't knock on this wood. A Canadian tourist mailed back a sliver of wood he had filched as a souvenir from the *Wasa*, a 17th-century ship being restored in Stockholm, Sweden.

The thief said his luck had soured since the theft. In a letter to the restorers, he related his woes:

I am normally not superstitious, but since I stole that little piece of wood from the ship I have been hit by bad luck, diseases, and disappointments. I had made it hardly 50 yards from the entrance of the Wasa *Shipyard when I discovered that a jar of syrup in my bag had broken. I have also been plagued by severe pain in my back and been betrayed in love and friendship. I hope that by returning it I will regain my good luck.*
                                    A Guilty Canadian.

Wasa was, in fact, a jinxed ship. Starting on her maiden voyage in 1628 as the king's flagship, she didn't make it out of Stockholm harbor. Horrified onlookers watched her capsize and sink. She was raised in 1961 after lying on the sea floor for 333 years.

Cross my heart.   A mugger with a fast tongue and slow wits promised to repay the two Jersey City women whom he robbed of $101.

To prove his good faith, he gave the women his name and address in Bangor, Maine.

A week later he still insisted he would pay back the $101.

"A promise is a promise," he said from his cell in the county jail.

Gone but not forgotten.   Someone stole the gumball machine from Jerry Pinter's coin laundry in Burlington, Wisconsin. Twenty-two years later, Pinter got a call from the thief, who wanted to make amends.

"I thought it was somebody trying to give me the business," said Pinter. "I couldn't believe it."

The caller asked the value of the machine in 1968, the year it was stolen. Pinter checked around and settled on $25.

The thief sent $118, saying in an unsigned letter that there was about $32 worth of gum and coins in the machine he stole. The rest was conscience money.

Better late . . . In 1982, ten dollars arrived at Loeb's Department Store in Lafayette, Indiana. The money was in a plain white envelope, along with a letter:

> *In the early 1930s I owed Loebs I think eighty-seven cents and never paid it. Occasionally thru the yrs, I think of the wrong I done, so am sending you ten dollars. Hope this will take care of interest and all. Hope you will forgive me. Thank you.*

The letter was without a signature, but the somewhat shaky handwriting was clearly a woman's.

"Nowadays, the store wouldn't even send out a bill for eighty-seven cents," said the store manager. "It wouldn't be worth it. For five dollars we probably wouldn't send one out. Back in the thirties, however, you could buy a towel for eighty-five cents or a pair of hose for fifty cents. That was the heart of the Depression, and whatever she bought probably meant a great deal to that woman at that time. It's quite possible she just didn't have the money to pay it off. When I think of the guilt trip she's had for more than fifty years. . . ."

Ring out the old. A pine tree belonging to Parker Everns of Chippewa, Wisconsin, was chopped down and carried off three days before Christmas.

Six weeks later the less-than-sorry thief returned it in a plastic bag with a note attached:

> *Dear Sir,*
> *Thanks for the use of the tree. It really made our Christmas. I wish you could have seen how we had it decorated up. I was looking at all the other trees in your yard and, with a little trimming on your part, one of them could qualify for our tree next Christmas. Thanks again. See you next year!*

You can say that again. A young man robbed a Cumberland Farms store in Manchester, New Hampshire. The next day he stuck his head in the door and told the clerk he was sorry.

Did he give back the money?

"He wasn't that sorry," said the clerk.

Change of heart. The Phoenix office of the FBI received a cardboard box filled with $36,000 in $100 bills. The sender explained in an unsigned note that the money was from a bank robbery in Gallup, New Mexico, plus interest. Two months earlier, a single gunman had bound and gagged the tellers in the Western Bank in Gallup and cleaned out the cash drawers.

And they always assumed it was a tree swallow. A guilt-ridden tourist who picked an orange from a grove in Santa Ana, California, mailed an apology and a one-dollar bill to the sheriff's department.

The note read:

> *I want to pay for the orange I picked along the highway in Orange County. I had this feeling that I must be in heaven with all these oranges growing, and I must have one. I am sorry. Please pass this on to some orange grower.*

The foot's on the other shoe. "I wouldn't be doing this but my kids are starving," a masked gunman said after robbing a shoe store in Cedar Rapids, Iowa. He gave the two clerks $20 each.

4.
You Can Bank on It

Safe and sorry. Safecrackers tried to blow open a safe in the Provinsbanken in Munkebo, Denmark. The safe survived, but the bank collapsed.

A lot of us know the feeling. A month after holding up a bank near Evanston, Illinois, the culprit came back and scolded the teller.

"You gave me too many one-dollar bills last time," he complained. "I don't want that many ones. Do it right this time."

Things are seldom what they seem. In Detroit, a bank robbery suspect being pursued by two armed guards dodged into what he thought was an apartment building. He wound up behind bars in nothing flat. The "apartment building" was a police station.

Run for the money.   Joseph Clemmer leaped over the counter of a bank in Lincoln, Nebraska, socked the teller, and gathered up $645.

So far, so good.

The problem started when Clemmer ran. Bank employees and customers ran, too. After him.

He threw some money at them. They just ran faster.

"Are you crazy?" he screamed. "Take the money!"

He jumped into a taxi. His pursuers pounded on the windows and shouted, "He's a thief!"

Pushing out the other side, he dropped more money and sprinted off. He got about 50 feet and was mobbed.

Police tied him to 20 holdups in the previous two months.

Now if he'd thrown banana skins . . .

Since you put it that way.   Kevin Otis of Glasgow, Scotland, had his heart set on becoming a bank robber, and he didn't care who knew it.

He pushed to the front of the line, but a bank official told him to wait his turn.

After a fidgety ten minutes, his big moment arrived. He stepped up to the teller and recited his piece: "Quick, all your money!"

Instantly an alarm rang. Otis scrammed, but was caught.

At the police lineup, the bank official was unable to identify him.

"Hey, what's the matter with you?" Otis shrieked. "Don't you recognize me?"

That was enough for the police.

Faint-hearted.   A shortage of nerve did in a dumbo who tried to hold up a bank in Spokane, Washington. Shaking all over, he pointed a toy gun at Winifred Owens, a teller, and stammered for her money.

When she said she didn't have any, he stopped shaking and fainted dead away.

Police found his getaway car parked near the bank. The doors were locked and the keys were inside.

Better watch out.   Worst performance by a singing Santa Claus occurred in Shreveport, Louisiana. A Santa in sunglasses relieved a bank there of $1,000 while softly croaking, "We wish you a merry Christmas, we wish you a merry Christmas."

Against all odds.   Two hoodlums with more luck than brains pulled a bank job and got away, despite themselves.

Wearing ski masks and dark blue jumpsuits, they cleaned out the teller drawers and a cash machine of a bank in Vancouver, British Columbia.

Once outside, they fastened shut the front doors of the bank with a heavy chain and padlock. That was supposed to keep everyone inside for a while — unless, of course, someone used the back door.

Determined not to be caught, the twosome coolly followed their carefully thought-out plan. They dropped boards spiked with nails in the parking lot. The nails pointed sharp end up to puncture the tires of vehicles giving chase.

Yep, you guessed right.

They ran over a board with their stolen getaway car. A flat tire stopped them a block and half from the bank.

When last seen, they were legging it across a field with the bank's money.

Cheers. After robbing a bank in Toronto, Canada, of $3,000, a thirsty gunman strolled down the street and into the corner tavern.

He bought drinks for everyone.

He was sitting at the bar with his new friends and the bag of money in front of him when police arrived.

Sacked for a loss. A fast-thinking teller in Columbia, South Carolina, foiled a robber with a question.

She read his note. *This is a stickup. I want all your money.* Flipping over the note, she wrote on the back, *Have you anything to put it in?*

The man read the question, shook his head ruefully, and high-tailed it for the door.

Wrong-way robber. A bearded gent pushed six $50 bills at a teller in Federal Savings and Loan in Akron and asked for three $100 bills.

As she began to peel off the bills, he fumbled on a ski mask and lowered a hand into his pocket as if reaching for a gun.

The teller promptly dropped out of sight behind the counter. The bearded man froze in dismay.

Then, completely rattled, he fled empty-handed, leaving behind the bank's money and his own six $50 bills.

Mask, and ye shall receive. In Yakima, Washington, many people wore paper masks to protect themselves from volcanic ash after Mount St. Helens erupted. A bank there posted a sign:

FOR SECURITY REASONS
PLEASE REMOVE MASKS BEFORE ENTERING

A little knowledge is a dangerous thing. A couple of armed chumps swept into what they thought was a bank in Montgomery, Alabama.

After madly pulling open drawers in the search for cash, they finally heeded what the employees were saying. It wasn't a bank anymore.

The dopey duo had stormed an accounting firm, which had occupied the premises for more than a month.

A novel approach. With the arrest of Mike Rodin in Dallas, the FBI at last had the bank robber famed for his lengthy holdup notes.

"Most notes say, *This is a stickup,* and ask for money," said an FBI agent. "This guy writes you a nice letter and then goes from there."

Sometimes it took bank tellers several minutes just to read Rodin's notes and figure out what he wanted.

No inventory. The demand was classic: "Give me all your money."

The response wasn't. The teller told the holdup man that the bank had no money.

No joke.

The bank, the Mellon Boulder Industrial Bank in Boulder, Colorado, had voluntarily liquidated its assets and had quit accepting deposits.

Decisions, decisions. The man had sat in his car for more than an hour in front of the Timewell State Bank in Timewell, Illinois. Finally the bank's president went outside and asked if he could be of help.

"Well, I'm not going to do it, but I've been debating whether or not to rob this bank," the man told him, and drove away.

Hi, remember me? "I just wanted to see if she'd recognize me," Allister Fallowfield told the police.

Two days after robbing a bank near London, Fallowfield had returned and inquired of the same teller about opening a savings account.

She recognized him.

Stalled. Despite having just heisted $13,492 from a bank in Portland, Oregon, Eddie Severen couldn't find change for a pay toilet in a nearby coin laundry. He didn't even have a one-dollar bill to feed the change maker.

He was flipping desperately through a wad of bills when a bank guard collared him.

Check point. Eunice Dunlop, a bank teller in Dundee, Scotland, had her checkbook stolen when her car was burglarized. The following month a customer gave her a check to cash.

"I thought," said Dunlop, "this is my check and it isn't my handwriting. Then it hit me — that's my check and it's stolen. I literally was ready to go over the counter after the guy."

Police saved her the trouble.

What a line. John Trent of Liverpool, England, had been standing in a line so long he wasn't in a mood for further delay.

When the man in front of him reached the teller and pulled a gun, Trent's patience ran out.

"Clear out!" he cried.

The startled gunman didn't argue. He cleared out.

It figures.   During the 1980s, bank robberies in the U.S. increased. So banks *decreased* the number of armed guards.

Sound crazy?

Bank officials had an excuse. The sight of a guard with a pistol on his hip, they said, raised the likelihood for violence.

An unstated reason for the cutback was the payroll. Bankers took to heart a 1986 report by the FBI. According to the FBI's figures, the average bank heist netted $5,251. The cost in wages of a full-time guard was higher.

Coffee break of the century.   Workers knocking down an old building in Macon, Georgia, discovered a 200-foot tunnel. It led across the street to the wall enclosing the vault in the Citizens & Southern Bank. No one knows when the tunnel was dug, or why it was abandoned so close to its objective, or who dug it.

"You'd like to have somebody that industrious working for you," said a bank vice-president.

Yawn stopper.   His audience was nodding off as a candidate for office in Milwaukee County, Wisconsin, droned on about the money that park water-slides had brought in while he was parks director.

"We've more than paid for two of those water-slides, and we've got —"

His next words snapped everyone awake.

"You guys have got a bank robbery across the street," he said, pointing to the First Wisconsin National Bank. He had glimpsed two masked men running from the bank. They got away with several thousand dollars.

"Now look," the candidate said. "I promised to bring excitement to county government, but this is ridiculous."

Let the good times roll. "Have a pleasant day," the man said to Claudia Clandon, 75, as he cut through her backyard in Chattanooga after robbing the bank next door.

Zzzzzz. Worn out by three hours of effort trying to break through the walls of a bank vault, L. Y. Innjui of Nairobi, Kenya, lay down for a snooze. He was still asleep, perhaps dreaming of a wild and carefree life, when police clapped him in 'cuffs.

Those were the days. Malcolm Pitts was the high-living cashier at the People's Bank of Portsmouth in Richmond, Virginia, in 1905. A five-year sentence for slipping $800,000 of the bank's funds into his pocket didn't dampen his style. He rode to the penitentiary in a private railroad car accompanied by 12 friends and one sheriff.

I just can't put my finger on it. A woman used her foot to rob the Standard Chartered Bank in Manama, Bahrain.

For several months Sari Haccera succeeded in beating the bank's system for helping its uneducated customers.

She doused her big toe in black ink and stepped on withdrawal slips, forging the thumbprints of folks who couldn't write their names.

She got $75,000 — and a three-month sentence.

Try a little tenderness. A young aircraft mechanic, bent on getting rich quick, pulled a gun on a teller in a bank in Jersey City. She refused to give him anything but a flat no.

He seemed more shocked at the sight of her than by her answer. He bolted, but didn't stay free for long.

The teller knew his name and his address. She once dated him.

Seemed like a good idea at the time. A robber walked into the same Alabama bank he had robbed before. He wore a stocking mask again and held the same weapon.

Well, hello and —

An FBI agent just happened to be showing his photograph to tellers who had witnessed the first robbery.

— Gotcha!

"His timing was the pits," said a bank officer.

Lemonaid. In Maryland a man rubbed his face with lemon juice because he'd been told it would keep bank cameras from picking up his picture. It didn't work, and the police made him come clean.

5.
Police Beat

Your thoughts are not my thoughts, neither are your ways my ways. In Philadelphia, a woman who sought to take the examination for police officer complained that all the test sites were in neighborhoods too dangerous to enter alone.

Meet me in Fort Wayne. You say you'd like to live in a place where folks are honest? Hustle over to Fort Wayne, Indiana.

Police there attempted to trap thieves by placing an expensive new TV set in an unlocked, parked car.

After a few weeks of watching from a van, the police gave up.

"People walked past the car, looked at the TV, opened the door, pushed the lock button down, closed the door, and walked on," a policeman said. "Nobody tried to take it."

Snooty Louise. In Hildesheim, West Germany, a female cop answered to the name of Louise and didn't mind being called a pig.

That's because she was one — a 220-pound wild boar.

Dressed in a snazzy harness, Louise was regularly used as a supersniffer. Her trainer, Werner Franke, maintained that Louise could outsniff any canine tracker.

"She can zero in on all known narcotics buried to a depth of four and a half feet," said Werner. "She can't be put off the scent by noises and other smells like dogs can.

"Further," he added, "pigs can sniff all day without rest and cover a lot of ground. It's their instinct. They are ideal for what we call large-area sniffing."

Purists in the Interior Ministry of Lower Saxony thought a pig was bad for the image of the force. They pressed for her retirement.

Instantly, pig lovers rose to her defense. Lower Saxony Premier Ernst Albrecht wrote a eulogy to her. Others called for "guard-pig units" to replace German shepherds.

So Louise's sizeable nose stayed on the job, and she received the title of *schuffelwildschwein*, or "sniffing wild boar."

She never hammed it up. She earned her 110 marks ($50) monthly. Most of it went for food.

"She did not take any old biscuit," said Franke. "Only the expensive Dutch ones with lots of chocolate coating or Danish butter cookies. I must have spoiled her."

Pounds were grounds. For safety's sake, the Washington, D.C., police placed a 195-pound limit on officers riding motor scooters. The next day nearly half the scooter patrol had to be grounded.

Where, oh, where are you? On April Fool's Day, Philadelphia police sent letters to hard-to-find former prisoners suspected of crimes since their release.

The letters told the ex-prisoners that the "Philadelphia Prison Reimbursement Fund," a made-up organization, owed them as much as $475 for their imprisonment.

The letter was mailed to 90 fugitives at their last known addresses and to their relatives and friends. Thirteen wanted men showed up at the Philadelphia Detention Center to pick up their cash and were immediately booked.

A detective said he got the idea from the police in Denver. They caught 67 fugitives the previous January by promising free football tickets.

Catch-as-catch-can.   Two officers pursuing a fugitive on a beach in Swansea, Wales, shouted, "Follow that man!"

The operator of a mechanical excavator obliged. He scooped up the officers with his huge shovel and put the ten-ton machine into high gear. It went fast enough to overtake the breathless theft suspect. Then it sank in the soft sand. High tide covered it.

The police got their man, and the construction company got a repair bill of $7,200.

Help wanted.   Rita Conrad of Perrine, Florida, wanted to become a policewoman. So she filled out an application. Her fingerprints revealed how badly the police wanted her, too. There were 11 bench warrants out on her.

A poultry offense. Police in Fort Fairfield, Maine, got wind of a stray chicken roosting in a car on Main Street. The police arrested the fowl offender and read it its rights.

The chicken went into the record as "Cee Little" of Main Street. The charges: criminal mischief, criminal trespass, public indecency, resisting an officer, and littering.

"It started out as a joke and shouldn't have gone as far as it did," said the officer. "But in a town like Fort Fairfield [population 4,300], you have to do something to keep from going crazy."

The next morning, the four-pound bird was released into the custody of a chap who liked eggs.

She didn't get ripped off.   A policewoman in New Orleans tore her trousers while chasing a teenage girl suspected in an auto theft. The policewoman filed suit against the girl's mother in small claims court for $31.86, the cost of the trousers.

To make amends for her daughter's conduct, the upset mother dropped $52 off at the court clerk's office.

"This is really terrific," said the happy policewoman. "You know, officers are always getting sued for harrassment when we're doing our jobs. Yet we have the same rights as any citizen. It's time we stand up and start using the laws to our own advantage."

Now you see it, now you don't.   The new 300-pound safe in the Cochran, Georgia, police department was stolen while the officers were on night patrol.

Police Academy.   In Manchester, England, an exercise to train policemen in riot control became too much like the real thing. Twenty officers were carted off to the hospital.

Making it.   Benjamin Ward was appointed New York City's Police Commissioner 40 years after being named "police commissioner for a day," the prize for winning a citywide essay contest.

His prize was a can of oil. RMI-3 received New York City's "Cop of the Month" award in 1984.

RMI-3 was a $22,000 robot. It stood four feet tall, had six wheels, one arm, and weighed 230 pounds.

The robot earned its award for work during a shootout between police and two gunmen holed up in an apartment in Elmira, New York.

It shoved open a door, scanned the apartment, and was guided into the bathroom. Its video camera showed both gunmen out of action.

The pictures sent by RMI-3 assured the lawmen that the danger was ended.

Many police departments have robots now, but RMI-3 is believed to be the country's first to be named "Cop of the Month."

And the winner is?   Everyone had fun at the policemen's annual ball in Meppen, West Germany.

There was one hitch. The door prizes were stolen. Not from the ball. *For* the ball.

An officer had robbed local stores for the prizes and forged receipts on a stolen typewriter.

What every good cop should know.   You better be an "A" student in high school if you want to be a policeman in Málaga, Spain.

Some 3,000 people once took a test for 47 police cadet openings in the city. More than 2,000 flunked.

The test included such questions as:

In what year was Julio Acosta president of Costa Rica?

What do Alaskan fur seals eat?

What is the official currency of Madagascar?

Despite an uproar of protests, Police Commissioner Jacinto Mera defended the exam. The answers, he said, were in high school textbooks.

What's my line?   The play was *The Hollow*, a murder mystery set in London, England.

During an evening performance in Miami, Florida, an urgent telephone call requested that a member of the audience, Police Captain Ron Finkiewicz, be notified of an emergency.

But how could they pass along the message to Finkiewicz without interrupting the play? No one connected with the theater knew him by sight.

The female lead solved the dilemma. She slipped the message into the dialogue.

"Oh, by the way, has Inspector Thorpe left yet?" she asked on stage.

"Yes, he has," another actor answered.

"Oh, that's a pity. I have a message for him from Captain Finkiewicz. His mother-in-law's home was broken into and she needs to get in touch with him right away."

Finkiewicz jumped up from his front-row seat. In the lobby he received details of the burglary. He hurried to investigate.

"It was so smooth it took a moment to sink in," he said later. "All of a sudden it dawned on me. The play was about a murder in London, not Poland. Why would there be someone with a Polish name like mine in it?"

6.
Courtroom Capers

Ooops. Johnny Ray Burr, on trial for robbing a furniture store in Kansas City, Kansas, fired his lawyers and pleaded his own case.

Burr was doing pretty well — till the store owner identified him as the robber.

Burr jumped up and screamed, "Liar! I should have blown your [censored] head off!"

He caught himself, thought, and added quickly, "If I'd been the one that was there."

The jury convicted him in 20 minutes.

They also drink a lot of coffee. A judge in Belo Horizonte, Brazil, swore he would never accept a woman juror. He gave his reasons: Women shouldn't work outside the house, women are emotionally fragile, and the courtroom's toilet is dirty.

Plea bargaining. Burglar Marvin Mills of New York City was sentenced to seven years in the clink.

Mills objected. Seven was his unlucky number.

"Your Honor," he said. "Would you make it eight?"

It wasn't the kind of request the judge, David Katz, heard every day. He retired to his chambers and pondered for half an hour before granting Mills the extra year.

With time off for good behavior? A court in Bangkok, Thailand, sentenced Thanes Kham, a hotel cashier, to 865 years in prison for swiping $12,044.

The court later had a change of heart. It lowered his sentence to 576 years.

What a rap. While a judge in an Oklahoma County District Court was trying a case, someone stole his gavel.

Oooh, when he got home. Judge Leonard Finster, a police magistrate in Chicago, Illinois, ordered an offender who couldn't pay a ten-dollar fine locked up. When Mrs. Finster, seated near the bar, shouted, "That's an outrage!" he fined her $25.

Five will get you ten. Diego Fernandez, a car thief in Valparaíso, Chile, went to court seeking to have his bond lowered. Judge Joaquin Montt agreed, lowering bond in one auto theft charge from $5,000 to $2,500, and from $7,500 to $2,500 in another.

Fernandez seemed satisfied. Once in his cell again, he began to brood, then to curse, then to threaten. Jailers dragged him back to the courtroom.

Judge Montt asked what was wrong.

Fernandez swore some and retorted, "If you ever want to tell me anything, mail it to me."

"I won't have to mail you this," the judge said. "I'm finding you in contempt of court. One year in jail!"

"Why not make it five!" Fernandez shouted.

"All right, five," the judge agreed.

"Why not ten?"

"Ten years it is."

"Go on, raise the bonds to fifty thousand," Fernandez dared.

The judge did better. He raised the bonds to $100,000 and sent Fernandez to jail for ten years.

Judge not. When some educated thieves in Mexico City learned the man they had robbed was a judge, they mailed back the money, $1,150, with an apology, "Pardon us. To err is human."

Cool, man. A fleet-footed robbery suspect ran from a San Francisco courthouse with the police hard on his heels.

One of the officers, Murray Burton, cut past a nearby hotel pool.

"He went that way, officer!" cried a man in the pool.

Burton pulled up. He ordered the man, who wore only boxer shorts, out of the pool.

"He might have got away with it if he had escaped in the summertime," said Burton. "But the temperature was sixty degrees, and he was the only one in the pool."

Book celler. Robert Reari of Harare, Zimbabwe, was writing a book when he was convicted of robbery and impersonating an officer.

"It looks as if you'll have to finish your book in prison," said Justice Wilson Sandura. He gave Reari plenty of time — four and a half years.

Reari had titled his book, *Crime Does Not Pay*.

Come clean. Judges in Rochester, New York, started a new program of sentencing. Instead of being fined or jailed, nonviolent lawbreakers were made to do community service.

One man, convicted of drunken driving, had to clean the elephant cage at the zoo.

His service was a one-way success. He rode the bus to work, but the driver wouldn't let him on when he finished his smelly job. He had to walk home.

He went ape.   Testifying against a drug dealer, an undercover police officer in Omaha, Nebraska, took the stand wearing a gorilla mask to hide his identity.

When the deputy police chief heard the officer was making a monkey of himself in court, he ordered him to find another disguise.

The following day the officer testified with a pillowcase over his head.

Nothing could be finer than to be in Carolina.   A circuit court judge in Union, South Carolina, fined himself for being 15 minutes late to court. He got stuck in traffic during the 60-mile drive from his home in Lexington.

"I can't expect anyone else to be on time and then I show up late," he said.

He sentenced himself to ten days in jail or a one-dollar fine. He paid the fine.

Show and tell. Holly Puig wore only a turban and the American flag stapled in front when she answered a shoplifting charge. "I love my country," she told the judge. The judge dressed down the Syracuse woman and gave her 30 days in jail for contempt of court.

7.
Behind Bars

Shucks, ask me a hard one. The Law Enforcement Assistance Administration once spent $27,000 of the taxpayers' money to find out why prisoners want to escape from jail.

Bingo! Gabriel Lopez didn't celebrate his 33rd birthday in the happiest of surroundings.

A cosmetics salesman, he was spending three years in prison at Punta Arenas, Chile, for passing $8,000 in bad checks.

But wait.

As a birthday present, a cellmate gave him a lottery card for the Chilean soccer championship series. Lopez filled it out, guessing correctly the results of all 13 games. He won $170,000.

According to the law in Chile, persons imprisoned for passing bad checks can be set free if they pay their debts.

For Lopez, it had been a happy birthday after all.

Investing in his future.   Prisoners on Rikers Island in New York City took a class in the stock market. One day the teacher passed around a stock certificate.

An inmate accused of forgery studied it a little too long. When he asked about the kind of ink and paper used to print it, a guard yanked it away.

Sink your teeth into this one.   Rafael Reyes, 62, of Rio Cuarto, Argentina, went back to jail because he couldn't chew.

Shortly after his imprisonment, he had to have his teeth pulled for health reasons. The prison dentist promised him a set of false teeth. When he was released, however, his gums were still naked.

Reyes told a judge in Pergamino he was ill because he couldn't gum his food fine enough to digest. His illness kept him from getting a job to pay for new choppers.

The judge directed the prison dentist to finish the job.

Said His Honor, "Every man has a right to bite," or words to that effect.

Reha*bill*itation.   Phony $100 bills circulating in Richmond, Virginia, drew an investigation by Secret Service agents. The bills were traced to crafty cons working in a print shop — at the Virginia State Penitentiary.

He should have had it delivered. Giuseppe Russo, a warden in Gissi, Italy, was sentenced to seven months in his own jail for freeloading.

Once a week he let his prisoners take him out for a pizza. After they had stuffed themselves, he allowed them to go home and sleep it off.

Police learned of his pizza night when a prisoner's mother complained her son had raised a ruckus in the living room.

Battery up! A power failure plunged the Idaho State Penitentiary into pitch-blackness. Quick-witted officials encircled the prison with cars and used their headlights to prevent escapes.

It's easy to be critical, but hard to be correct. Klaus Kramer of Dortmund, West Germany, spent two years in jail because of his nose.

Kramer had been sentenced to six years mainly because of photographs of a huge-nosed man sticking up a bank, and the testimony of witnesses.

A court-appointed schnoz expert said uh-uh. Kramer's nose was definitely not the one snapped by the bank's automatic camera.

Kramer was released, and for each day in jail he received four dollars.

Soft cell. In 1985, the opening of the new El Dorado County jail in California had to be delayed. The cell doors didn't lock.

Return to sender. The customer relations boss at a mail-order house was surprised to get back an order of Special Forces-type boots and a lined poncho.

The merchandise had been shipped to a Richard Seward at an address that turned out to be the Mississippi State Prison. Seems prison officials, who check all packages, didn't want Seward or any other inmate preparing for a long hike.

Hard to stomach. Smoking can be bad for your health and happiness, especially if you have to cough up cash for a pack of cigarettes as Oscar Heath did.

On his first day in the Grand Traverse County jail in Traverse City, Michigan, he inquired if smokes were to be had.

The guards said sure. But he'd have to come up with a dollar a pack.

Heath obliged, nearly. He coughed up a ten-dollar bill, which he had wrapped in a plastic bag and gulped down earlier.

He tried again and pulled a $20 bill from his mouth.

Anyone who has ever kept money in his stomach can understand Heath's problem. It's so hard to find the right change.

Under prison rules, inmates' money had to be kept by prison officials, and not in stomachs. Heath was charged with possessing illegal goods.

He was already serving sentences for grand larceny and for shoplifting a can of chocolate syrup.

Dialing out.   Inmates in the Orange County jail in California used the jail telephones to shorten their sentences.

Pretending to be state correctional officials, they spoke to judges and won early releases.

Bare walls do not a prison make.   Prisoners in England's Haverigg Prison are a quick-tempered lot.

Make that hot-tempered.

They set a fire that gutted the kitchen, clothing

exchange store, education departments, and several wings. Sixteen men escaped during the rioting.

What started it all?

An unbearable injustice.

The prisoners were told to remove pinups from freshly painted walls.

8.
Aw-a-a-ay We Go!

Whistle while you work.   Prisoners in Israel's Ramallah prison were hours away from breaking out.

They never made it.

Blame their singing. It sounded like a flock of birds chirping off-key.

The warden, Muphid Abas, grew curious. He sneaked close and spied the jailbirds chipping a hole ·in a cell wall with metal slabs from their beds. The noise of the work was drowned out by the noisier songfest.

Abas put an end to both chipping and chirping.

The hole-in-the-wall gang.   In Wisconsin the warden of the Dane County jail had all posters taken down from cell walls and ceilings after three inmates escaped through a hole covered by a pinup.

Dead giveaway.   Hilary Sherman shipped out of a Vancouver Island prison in a coffin.

The coffin was a prop in the play *Dracula*, staged by fellow convicts. After the applause, Sherman stole the coffin, roped it to a homemade catamaran, and paddled his way to freedom.

It suited him.   An inmate with an eye for the correct traveling clothes made it look easy. He sawed the bars in the showers of the Florida State prison, slipped through a gate that led to the front gate, and strolled out.

He wore a coat and a hat and had painted his prison pants and shirt brown to resemble a guard's uniform.

Leave well enough alone.   Sam Ryan of Winnipeg, Canada, was locked up for forging a $600 check. He escaped, and it was three days before anyone noticed he was missing.

He might be free today except for wanting what was his. He returned to the city jail to pick up his wallet, which had been confiscated when he was arrested.

Stop payment!   Michigan officials discovered that 92 escaped prisoners were receiving welfare checks.

The truth will set you free.   Police helped robbers break *out* of a tavern in Reno, Nevada.

Two young women had hidden in a storeroom at closing time. All went well until they tried to leave with their loot. The place was rigged like Fort Knox to prevent illegal entries — and exits. They had to telephone for help.

Personal best.   Antonio D'Allessio paid for the damages he caused while busting out of jail in Milan, Italy.

D'Allessio and another prisoner smashed through the ceiling and roof on their route to freedom. Later D'Allessio telephoned a prison official to find out the amount of the damages. It was more than $500. He sent his check.

That wasn't the first time D'Allessio had made

good. He had inherited "a lot of money," according to his attorney, while in a lockup near Novara. He did about $300 in damages there during an unsuccessful breakout attempt. He had his attorney send a check to cover the cost of the repairs.   '

After the Milan escape, D'Allessio was recaptured and shifted to a top security prison.

Bar none.   In 1984, four prisoners escaped from a jail in Oristano, Sardinia. Their method was a textbook example of old-fashioned know-how.

The foursome cut through the bars of their cell with a file that a relative had delivered in a loaf of bread. Then they dropped to the ground by means of a knotted bed sheet.

The red-faced guards refused comment.

Nice try.   John Scott was the only man to break out of Alcatraz and live to tell of it.

In 1984, twenty-two years later, marathon swimmers Dave Horning and Randy Williams celebrated the anniversary of Scott's feat. They re-created his swim across the two-and-one-half miles of icy, shark-filled water from Alcatraz Island to San Francisco.

Both men utterly exhausted themselves, and Williams was treated for hypothermia.

Even so, they were more successful than Scott, who hadn't been able to make good his escape. The cops had welcomed him with open handcuffs as he staggered ashore.

Hey, pinhead.   Alf Reiner wriggled through a five-inch-wide window in his holding cell in Edmonton, Canada.

"You've got to see the guy's head to believe it," said a corrections officer. "The escape was the talk of the prison, especially how stupid he was to get caught less than two hours later."

Hi ho, hi ho, it's off to jail we go, again.   Ben Garland and Willie Winslow were a couple of long-termers at a state prison in Huntsville, Texas. While unloading furniture in the woodshop, they got this great idea. Use the trailer-truck they were unloading to escape.

The truck drove off with them in back. Fifteen miles down the road it stopped — inside another unit of the state prison system.

Power of the press.   Guards at the main jail in Oslo, Norway, didn't know of a prisoner's escape until a newspaper informed them.

Acting on a tip, a reporter for *Verdens Gang,* Norway's biggest daily, called the jail and said Erik Larsen had cut the bars of his cell window and slid to freedom down a rope.

The reporter met with disbelief until a guard looked into Larsen's cell.

"We consider the man to be dangerous," said Oslo's police chief, Magnar Aukrust.

All's fare . . . Manfred Bach skipped out of a minimum security prison in Stillwater, Minnesota, on Christmas Eve. He waved down a taxi and had the cabbie drive him 110 miles to his mother's house.

Lacking the Christmas spirit of giving, Bach refused to tip the cabbie. He also refused to pay the $125 fare.

The cabbie tipped the police. Bach's return trip was made in a squad car.

Genius at work. Kyle Hogan strolled into a Savannah police station. He had a little problem. He'd lost his identification card. Could anyone tell him how to replace it?

Good question, wrong place.

The police checked his identity with the National Crime Information Center, which listed him as an escapee from a Georgia prison.

He received a replacement identification card — in prison.

9.
Alibi Ikes

Pipe dream.   Two men who broke into a church near Frankfort, Indiana, told police they only wanted to play the organ.

A loaf of bread, a jug of wine?   Four cons in a Wyoming state prison swore to a judge that what they'd dug under the floor of their cellblock wasn't a tunnel but a wine cellar.

That certain feeling.   An ex-policeman of Carlow, Ireland, blamed his burglaries on eating too many doughnuts. The doughnuts brought on ups and downs in his blood-sugar levels, leading to "wicky-wacky" behavior, he claimed.

The judge saw the hole in his story and sentenced him to seven to fifteen years.

That's off (not over) the wall. While awaiting sentencing on a burglary charge, Harmon Tully escaped over the wall of a jail in San Francisco. Recaptured, he told the judge: "I was playing pole vault and I got too close to the wall and fell over. When I regained my senses, I ran around trying to find my way back in. I got lost. The next thing I knew I was in Los Angeles."

What'd he say? A Rhode Island man driving a stolen car was pulled over by a police officer. "Please don't arrest me," pleaded the car thief. "I stole it to go to court to answer a burglary charge."

Well, mow me down. A Washington man was fined $65 for shooting his lawnmower with a .357 caliber magnum pistol. He told the judge that he got angry when it wouldn't start, and it still won't.

A flue-ky story. A youth who got stuck in the chimney of a country club outside St. Louis said he was only trying to make a delivery.

Nailed. Sandy Miller, a manicurist from Trenton, New Jersey, said she had become a millionaire through meditation.

The jury said her forefinger was responsible and found her guilty of grand theft.

Miller had hit upon a glitch in her bank's computer program. Regularly she punched in hefty sums on the automatic teller without depositing a cent.

Cry panic. A New City attorney, arrested for leaping over a subway turnstile, claimed he was trying to make it to the church on time for his wedding.

Fiddling with the truth. Jarvis Colby, an American violin maker living in France, insisted he didn't steal a helicopter. "I was forced at gunpoint to fly that chopper," he said. "After I was freed, I didn't return it because I didn't want to miss dinner."

The savings and loan diet.   A car salesman on trial for bank robbery in Cleveland claimed he went to a hypnotist in an effort to lose weight, and the hypnotist left him with an overpowering urge to rob a bank.

Daddy Ghostbucks.   Cynthia Brandon of Denver said her father's ghost persuaded her to steal $50,000 from her former boss. The judge dismissed the case against the ghost but gave Brandon 20 years.

10.
For the Record

Open-door policy. After being burglarized 36 times in three years, Jim Barton, a 72-year-old news vendor of Bethnal Green, England, stopped locking his room. He had nothing left worth stealing.

The awful truth. In 1985, Katie Smith, a London pickpocket, was picked up by the bobbies for the 31st time. During a life of crime that dated back to 1926, the frail 75-year-old widow had spent 20 years in prison.

"My fingers are not as good as they used to be," Katie wheezed. "I'm retiring."

I smell a rat. Do crooks have a special air about them?

Before you turn up your nose at that idea, pay attention. Researchers at Leeds University in England are into "odorprints."

They're bottling the scent from the bodies of volunteers.

"Folks at the hospital tend to look at me a bit strangely," admits one of the researchers, Barbara Sommerville.

She claims everyone has an individual odor, criminals included. The main problem is finding a sensitive, reliable smell-detector.

Under consideration is the use of antennas of mosquitoes and flies. The little buggers are really good smellers.

Even if the odorprints are developed, the way to beat the new style of law and odor is foreseen.

The bad guys will drench themselves with after-shave lotions, colognes, and deodorants.

"England may someday have the sweetest-smelling criminals the world has ever sniffed," said Sommervile.

Tale of the tape. Police asked Maurice C. Snow to describe the man who had bound, gagged, and robbed him.

"Of course," agreed Snow, a shopkeeper in Worcester, Massachusetts, who provided this portrait:

The robber was 5 foot 10 and weighed between 165 and 170 pounds. His neck was 14½ inches and his sleeve 25½ inches. He had a 39-inch chest, a 34-inch waist, and 41-inch hips.

The description, said the police, was the most detailed they'd ever got from a victim.

And why not? Before he was robbed of a camera, a watch, and $24, Snow had measured the man for a suit.

They like it like that.   The custom of taking off one's shoes before entering a home is so strong in Korea that even burglars do so before breaking in.

Fighting for dollars.   Is a black eye worth it? For centuries the question floated from person to person without a definite opinion.

In 1988, the British government nailed down the answer.

A genuine shiner is worth $168.

The sum is part of the price list of punches the Home Office gave out to judges. Now toughs must pay folks they beat up on.

A slight puffing from a grazing swing brings a mere $84. One eye closed and blackened earns you $168. Really get worked over — limp out of the hospital with your head in a cast, say — and you can look forward to a soothing $2,940.

Ho, ho, ho. Some of the world's best pickpockets are trained at "The School of Ten Bells" in Bogotá, Colombia. The tuition is more than $3,000, and the final exam is a ding-a-ling.

A mannequin is dressed in a three-piece suit with sleighbells hung on the ten pockets. To graduate, the student has to empty the pockets without raising a tinkle.

A penny saved. In 1984, Hope Denner of Bend, Oregon, paid the heaviest fine in the history of the state.

The sum, $505, was for eluding police. To pay it, she saved her pennies for five years.

Two friends helped her carry 1,010 rolls of pennies — 455.6 pounds — to the courthouse, and lay them on the desk of the county clerk.

He said Denner was 46 cents shy.

Going one better. Artist Brett Wynn of West Palm Beach, Florida, presented the police with a signed, framed 24-by-30-inch oil painting of the man who ripped off his $1,000 gold neckchain.

Go fight city hall. An 80-year-old man tried to hold up a post office in downtown Jacksonville, Florida.

"You're out of luck," said a clerk. "The counters aren't open yet."

The man knew better than to reason with a government employee. He lowered his head forlornly and tottered away.

Now they tell us. A sign in a Tokyo hotel room was widely reprinted in the United States.

IS FORBIDDEN TO STEAL TOWELS, PLEASE.
IF YOU ARE NOT PERSON TO DO SUCH
PLEASE DO NOT READ NOTICE.

Sorry, wrong number. In 1981, teenager Barry Donaldson hopped on his motorcycle and set off for a Sunday spin in Parma, Ohio.

Police stopped him for changing lanes without signaling.

The next thing he knew, his bike was being towed away. He was taken to the police station and charged with possession of stolen property.

Ten days later, a patient detective proved Donaldson's motorcycle was not stolen. A manufacturer's error was at fault.

In 1976 the same serial number had been stamped on the frame of two bikes at the Kawasaki factory. Both were model KZ-900, and they had the same features and color.

"A one-in-a-million chance," said the detective. "In fact, the odds are probably even greater than that."

One of the motorcycles was stolen in 1977. The other wound up in a cycle shop in Milan, Ohio. Donaldson bought it fourth-hand for $1,700, two weeks before his arrest.

His innocence was established because the two bikes had different engine serial numbers.

Bad news came with the good. He had to pay $70 in storage fees to get the motorcycle back.

Lettuce now praise the refrigerator. To help the homeowner foil robbers, a company in Torrance, California, introduced a $15 head of lettuce made of vinyl. Inside was a jar to hold cash and other valuables.

"We got the idea after someone mentioned a burglary where everything was cleaned out but the refrigerator," said Gary Northrop, the sales manager.

The light that failed. The government of Taiwan banned video game arcades. A spokesman said some children had become juvenile delinquents, "stealing, robbing, and fighting" after they got hooked on the games.

In England you can see trees with proper pedigrees. Trees planted in a new industrial park in Birmingham, England, were selected for their slender trunks. City planners didn't want muggers to hide behind them.

Homeowners insurance. Eighty-year-old Arnold Clinton of New Orleans had a hunch his home would be robbed while he was on vacation.

So before leaving, the retired seaman left money, a bottle of whiskey, and a note on the kitchen table. The note read:

> *To the Burglar:*
> *Here is 51 dollars and about 30 or 40 dollars in change. Also a bottle of whiskey. All yours. There is no need to ransack the house looking for more money as it's all here. Don't be a jerk and steal anything. Be honest.*

Upon his return, Clinton discovered the thief had followed instructions. He took the money and left the whiskey and everything else in the house untouched.

High risk.   A convicted counterfeiter, now a businessman in Fort Worth, Texas, discussed the perils of his former profession.

"Counterfeiting tens and twenties isn't worth the effort and the risks," he said. "You have to keep moving from one store to another. This increases the danger because you are forced to deal with people you can't trust."

Body works.   If Air Force Major Fred Murphy has the same luck in the air as he does on the ground, he may be America's next ace.

He was shot at close range by a robber. The bullet bounced off his chest.

Murphy, who was stationed at Langley Air Force Base in Virginia, was held up by two men at the automatic teller of the Virginia National Bank. He gave them his money, but one of them pulled the trigger just the same.

The bullet left a bruise on his chest and burns on his coat. When Murphy just stood there, the robbers fled.

Did Murphy chase them?

"Are you crazy?" he said.

Modern job.   Luis Ortez of Miami, Florida, was told to wait in a room in headquarters for questioning in connection with a barroom brawl.

He waited patiently.

Saturday came and went. So did Sunday and Monday.

People asked, "What are you doing here?"

"I'm waiting for Detective Rodriguez," he replied.

He was told to stay where he was.

Tuesday passed. He'd had nothing to eat or drink. When he had to use the bathroom, he requested permission.

Wednesday he inquired if Detective Rodriguez was ever going to question him.

That's when someone thought to ask how long he'd been waiting.

How long?

Turned out Ortez had not been charged. An officer had been ordered to drive him home on Saturday. The officer went to the wrong room. Someone else got the ride.

For his five-day wait, Ortez accepted a $2,500 settlement from the city.

I'll grab the dough, Fred, you do the driving. By 1982, the economy in England had fallen so low that some criminals couldn't afford a getaway car.

A couple of hoods held up a North London post office and got $4,000. Then they jumped on a bicycle. One pedaled like mad while the other sat on the handlebars and waved a sawed-off shotgun.

Surprise. To thwart purse-snatchers, an inventor in Detroit designed a handbag that falls apart if tugged.

Never drink alone. Roland Weeks, an Irish safe-cracker, needed a drink to steady his nerves.

One drink led to another. . . .

A security guard in a Dublin office building found him snoring by the safe, his burglar's tools strewn over the floor, a half-empty bottle of wine by his chair.

Because all books should have a happy ending. A Kansas man and woman met when he commandeered her car at pistolpoint with the police hot on his heels. The couple announced plans to marry while he served a one- to five-year sentence for burglary.

Solution to
The Case of the
Two-Headed Toothbrush

Bugs knew nothing about coin laundry machines. So he simply repeated what Melvin told Encyclopedia.

Melvin, who was washing clothes, said, "I had the lid of the machine raised and was pushing the laundry down inside it with both hands. . . ."

Bugs told the same story. However, he changed one fact so it wouldn't seem as if he were just mouthing Melvin's account.

Bugs said he was *drying* clothes.

That was his mistake!

Encyclopedia whispered into his ear, "You lift the *lid* and push clothes *down* only in a washing machine. A dryer doesn't have a lid on top. It has a door in the side."

Bugs couldn't have dried his clothes in a washing machine!

ENCYCLOPEDIA BROWN CARRIES ON

Donald J. Sobol

Interior illustrations by
IB OHLSSON

For Joan and Dick Dorff

The Case Of the Giant Mousetrap

Idaville!

Crooks turned pale at the mention of the town. They knew what to expect there — a fast trip to jail.

No one, grown-up or child, got away with breaking the law in Idaville.

Police across the nation wondered. How did Idaville do it? What was the secret behind its record of law and order?

Idaville looked like many other seaside towns. It had lovely beaches, three movie theaters, and four banks. It had churches, a synagogue, and two delicatessens.

And, of course, it had a police station. But that was not the real headquarters of the war on crime. A quiet red brick house on Rover Avenue was.

In the house lived Encyclopedia Brown, America's Sherlock Holmes in sneakers.

Mr. Brown, Encyclopedia's father, was chief of

police. He was brave and smart. But once in a while he came across a case that no one on the force could crack.

When that happened, Chief Brown knew what to do. He went home.

At the dinner table he told the facts to Encyclopedia. One telling was enough. Before the meal was over, Encyclopedia had solved the mystery for him.

Chief Brown was proud of his only child. He wanted it written in every school book: "The greatest detective in history wears sneakers to work."

But who would believe such a statement?

Who would believe that the brains behind Idaville's crime clean-up was ten years old? History wasn't ready for that.

So Chief Brown said nothing.

Encyclopedia never let slip a word about the help he gave his father. He didn't want to seem different from other fifth graders.

But there was nothing he could do about his nickname. He was stuck with it.

Only his parents and his teachers called him by his real name, Leroy. Everyone else called him Encyclopedia.

An encyclopedia is a book or set of books filled with all kinds of facts. Just like Encyclopedia's head.

Encyclopedia had read more books than anyone in Idaville, and he never forgot what he read. You might say he was the only library in America whose

116

steps left footprints with a saw-toothed tread.

At the dinner table one Friday night, Chief Brown stirred his soup slowly. It was a sign that Encyclopedia and his mother knew well. A case was troubling him.

After a moment Chief Brown put down his spoon and said, "Salvatore Custer is at it again."

"Oh, no," groaned Encyclopedia.

Salvatore was an unemployed inventor and artist. He lived in Idaville six months of the year. The rest of the time he spent hanging his paintings in museums. Authorities removed them the instant they were discovered.

"Do you know the old saying, 'Build a better mousetrap and the world will beat a path to your door'?" asked Chief Brown. "Salvatore thought it said *bigger* mousetrap."

Chief Brown explained. Salvatore had built a mousetrap eight feet long, six feet wide, and five feet high. It had a motor and wheels, and it could go faster than a speeding mouse.

A museum of art in New York City had been interested for a while. But the museum had wounded Salvatore's pride. It had asked him to pay the shipping cost.

Next he had tried an exterminating company. He had thought the mousetrap would make good advertising. Turned down, he had parked his creation on the front lawn at City Hall.

"The problem," said Chief Brown, "is that no one

wants it there, and yet no one wants to move it. Salvatore won't drive it off—or rather, he's unable to. He hid the key and now he can't find it."

"How absolutely wild," said Mrs. Brown. "Why did he hide the key?"

"He was angry at the world for refusing his art," said Chief Brown, taking a notebook from his breast pocket. "Maybe you can help, Leroy. I wrote down everything Salvatore told me."

Using his notes, Chief Brown related what had happened.

About one o'clock that afternoon, Salvatore left the mousetrap in front of City Hall. "It's my gift to Idaville," he announced bitterly.

Just then a police car pulled up. Salvatore thought he was about to be arrested. Frightened, he fled into City Hall, hoping to escape through the rear exit.

In the lobby, he slipped on the marble floor. His head banged against a pillar. Dazed, he made his way unsteadily to the bank of elevators, which was nearer than the rear exit.

He remembered that in the subbasement there was a stairway that led up to Fourth Street at the side of the building. It seemed to him the best means of getting away.

As he rode dizzily down in the elevator, he grew angry. People had laughed enough at his art and inventions. He decided to strike back.

When he got off the elevator, he hid the ignition

118

key to the mousetrap. He put it in one of the trash boxes standing in a corner. If the police caught him, they would not find it.

The elevator car he had ridden was one of two that serviced the underground floor. He had just hidden the key when he saw the other elevator coming down. The police, he thought, were in full chase.

He was still dizzy, and he realized that he had no chance of outrunning his pursuers. So he decided not to use the stairs to Fourth Street.

He pressed the "up" button on the wall. The doors of his elevator opened, and he took it to the second floor. From there he hurried down the fire stairs to the ground floor and escaped out the rear exit.

Chief Brown closed his notebook. "That's about all of it," he said. "I found Salvatore at his sister's house. He was sorry about hiding the key, but it is too late."

"Why?" asked Mrs. Brown.

"The subbasement is the only floor that's cleaned out on Fridays. All the trash there—including the box with the key—was trucked to the dump and burned."

"Is the key really so important?" said Mrs. Brown. "Why can't the mousetrap be pushed off the lawn?"

Chief Brown chuckled. "When Salvatore hid the key, he may have been dizzy. But he was clearheaded about city government."

120

"I don't understand," said Mrs. Brown.

Chief Brown took a deep breath. "The police department won't touch the mousetrap. We claim it's the job of the department of parks. They say it's the job of the department of roads. It may be the job of the fire department or the dog pound. The mayor is looking up the law."

"Then the mousetrap will stay on the lawn for weeks," said Mrs. Brown.

Chief Brown nodded. "There the thing sits, right in the middle of town, waiting for a mouse the size of a dragon. It's Salvatore's revenge."

A long silence fell upon the room. Mrs. Brown glanced at Encyclopedia. He had not asked his one question. Usually he needed but one question to solve a case.

He had closed his eyes. He always closed his eyes when he did his heaviest thinking.

Suddenly his eyes opened. He asked his question.

"How many floors are there in City Hall, Dad?"

Chief Brown thought for a moment. "There's the subbasement at the bottom . . . and then the basement. Above ground are five floors."

"What does that have to do with the problem, Leroy?" asked Mrs. Brown. "The problem is to get the mousetrap moved."

"I just wanted to be certain there wasn't another floor below the subbasement," replied the boy detective.

His parents looked at him, puzzled.

"The key wasn't taken to the dump," said Encyclopedia. "It's still where Salvatore put it."

WHAT MADE ENCYCLOPEDIA SO SURE?

(Turn to page 175 for the solution to "The Case of the Giant Mousetrap.")

The Case of Bugs Meany, Thinker

During the summer, Encyclopedia solved cases for the children of the neighborhood.

As soon as school let out, he set up a detective agency in the garage. Every morning he hung out his sign:

BROWN DETECTIVE AGENCY
13 Rover Avenue
Leroy Brown, President
No Case Too Small
25¢ Per Day
Plus Expenses

The first customer on Monday morning was Winslow Brant. Winslow was Idaville's master snooper. He snooped in trash piles all over town.

If he found something old and interesting, he fixed it up. Then he sold it at a flea market.

"I want to hire you," he said to Encyclopedia. "I think Bugs Meany smooth-talked me out of a cut-glass lamp."

Bugs Meany was the leader of a gang of tough older boys. They called themselves the Tigers. They should have called themselves the Elbow Bands. They were always up to something crooked.

"I found the lamp in Mrs. Bailey's trash last week," said Winslow. "It must be seventy-five years old and worth a lot to anyone who likes old lamps."

"Bugs stole it?" asked Encyclopedia.

"In a way," said Winslow. "I was taking it home when I met him. He told me he'd give me a Doctor of Philosophy diploma for it — if I was smart enough."

"Come again?" said Encyclopedia.

"Bugs tested my brains," Winslow went on. "He asked me: 'If Y equals Z times X, how long would it take a woodpecker to drill a hole through a kosher pickle?' I got the answer."

"You did?"

"I said the problem couldn't be solved without knowing the thickness of the pickle and the length of the woodpecker's beak. Bugs shook my hand. He said I could take his course in deep thinking."

Encyclopedia groaned. "On graduation, you'd get a Doctor of Philosophy diploma. And all Bugs wanted in return was the lamp."

"Right," said Winslow. "I thought of how proud my folks would be of their nine-year-old son the doctor. But I think Bugs put one over on me."

He laid twenty-five cents on the gas can beside Encyclopedia. "I want you to get back my lamp. Bugs said he'd return it if I wasn't completely satisfied with my progress."

"In that case, I'll see what I can do," replied Encyclopedia. He had handled Bugs and his Tigers in the past.

The Tigers' clubhouse was an unused toolshed behind Mr. Sweeney's Auto Body Shop. On the way there, Winslow explained about the deep-thinking course.

Bugs had told him to start slowly—say, one thought a day. After six weeks, a student should be having two-and-a-half thoughts a day. Even if they were always the same thoughts, they would be enough to earn a diploma as a Doctor of Philosophy.

When Encyclopedia and Winslow arrived at the Tigers' clubhouse, they found Bugs inside practicing his penmanship. He was learning to write excuse notes in his mother's handwriting.

"We came for Winslow's lamp," said Encyclopedia.

"Your thinking course is a big fat fake," added Winslow.

"What? What is this I hear?" gasped Bugs. "How is it possible? I myself got into deep thinking only three months ago. Already I am a new man."

"It hasn't done a thing for me," said Winslow.

125

"Perhaps you didn't heed my advice, dear lad," said Bugs, in a hurt voice. "If you put your mind to it, it will change your entire life and earn you a diploma."

"Just give me back my lamp," insisted Winslow.

Bugs lifted his gaze as though praying for patience.

"Did I try to sell you one of those new thinking caps, the ones with the orange and white racing stripes?" he asked. "No, no, no! All I asked was that you wear loose, comfortable clothes. And avoid tight shoes at all costs."

"You didn't have to sell me anything," said Winslow. "You took my lamp."

"Lamp?" exclaimed Bugs. "What lamp?"

"The cut-glass lamp I traded for your phoney course," said Winslow. "Maybe you forgot Mr. Stevens. He was cutting his grass when I handed the lamp to you. He saw us."

Bug's eyes squinted shut as though he'd been whacked on the nose.

"Don't faint on me," said Winslow.

"I was merely pausing in memory of all the sardines caught off the coast of Alaska," explained Bugs calmly.

"Huh?" muttered Winslow.

"Wait a second. . . . I seem to recall such a lamp," said Bugs. He breathed a sigh of regret. "Alas, it is no more."

"What happened to it?" demanded Encyclopedia.

"Sunday I was taking it to the flea market," said Bugs. "I was sitting with it in the cargo space of my uncle's truck. Suddenly the truck stopped for a traffic light—*screech!* The lamp flew back over the tailgate. It landed on the street—*smash!*

Bugs grinned at Encyclopedia, double-daring the boy detective to prove the story untrue.

Encyclopedia grinned back.

"Sorry, Bugs," he said. "You won't get me to fall for that one. Better take another course in deep thinking."

WHAT WAS BUGS'S MISTAKE?

(Turn to page 176 for the solution to "The Case of Bugs Meany, Thinker.")

The Case of the Grape Catcher

Bugs Meany thought a great deal about Encyclopedia's teeth.

The Tigers' leader longed to knock them so far that people a mile away would start dressing Christmas trees, thinking it was snowing.

Bugs hated being outsmarted time after time. He wanted to get even. But he didn't dare use muscle. Whenever he had that urge, he remembered Sally Kimball.

Sally was Encyclopedia's junior partner. She was also the prettiest girl in the fifth grade and the best athlete. More than once she had done the impossible. She had punched out Bugs Meany!

Because of Sally, Bugs never dared hit Encyclopedia. He never stopped planning his revenge, however.

"Bugs won't rest till he gets back at you, Encyclopedia," warned Sally.

129

"And at you," added Encyclopedia. "He tells everyone that he won't hit a girl. He says that he lets you win."

"Sour grapes," snorted Sally. "Speaking of grapes—my goodness!—I'm due at Edsel Wagonbottom's house right now. He wants me to pitch grapes to him."

Encyclopedia went with her. There was no way he would be left behind.

The Wagonbottoms owned a fruit company and lived in a large house on three acres. Edsel, a cocky fifth grader, met the detectives by the front steps. He held a bowl of grapes.

"I want to hire you for three or four hours," he said to Sally. "You have the best arm in school, and I use only the best."

He took the detectives around to the backyard. It was enclosed by thick hedges. In one corner stood a tennis court. Near the house was a swimming pool. Enough space was left over for a football field.

Edsel handed the bowl to Sally. "Throw me a grape," he said.

He jogged out twenty feet, hands at his sides, and turned. Sally forward-passed a green grape. Too low. Edsel lunged, missed.

"Don't throw on a straight line," he called impatiently. "Get more height."

Sally obeyed. After a few throws, she got the hang of it. Edsel caught every one in his mouth—glop, schlurp, swallow.

The day was very hot, and they took several

breaks. "I'd invite you to swim, but we just had the pool repaired," said Edsel. "It's still being filled."

Water was pouring from a pipe at one end of the pool and from a garden hose. The three children ran the cold water from the hose over their heads to cool off.

Then Sally resumed throwing. Edsel would race across the grass, turn, and wait for the throw, mouth open. He always made the play.

At the end of two hours, they stopped for lunch.

"The maid is off and my folks are away," said Edsel. "You'll have to eat frozen dinners."

While Sally and Encyclopedia fixed the meal, Edsel explained about his gifted mouth.

For two years he had performed at outings for the employees of his father's fruit company. But he had really come into his own earlier in the summer. The mayor had thrown out a grape to start the midget baseball league. It was a bad throw, but Edsel had caught it, no-handed.

"I'm ready to go nationwide," he boasted. "I'll be at the Fruit Growers meeting in Chicago next month. I figure to set an American record for boys — two hundred feet, hand to mouth."

After lunch, Edsel let Sally clean up the kitchen, and then they continued practicing. At two o'clock he brought out more grapes.

"Let's drill for quickness," he said. He turned off the garden hose and pulled the free end from the pool.

"Tie me up," he directed Encyclopedia. "I want to

practice catching without using my legs."

Encyclopedia tied Edsel with the hose. For a few minutes Sally threw from ten feet. Unable to move, Edsel missed frequently.

Suddenly Officer Carlson stepped into the backyard. Bugs Meany dashed out of the house.

"You see it, officer!" he screamed. "They're torturing this poor boy!"

The policeman looked uncertain.

"I came over to visit my pal, Edsel," Bugs went on. "What did I find? He was tied up like that. These two were hitting him with grapes and laughing. I had to call the police."

Officer Carlson untied Edsel. "Is this true?" he asked.

"It's true, I swear it!" gasped Edsel. He fell on the ground as if too weak to stand. "They tied me up and threw grapes at me for hours and hours."

"The inhuman fiends!" cried Bugs. "Torturing him in the hot, cruel sun! How he must have suffered!"

Edsel moaned. "They ganged up on me. Everyone knows what a dirty fighter the girl is. . . . Oooh. . . . Aaah."

"This is a frame-up!" Sally protested to Officer Carlson. "Bugs is trying to get us in trouble. He wants to get even. Edsel is helping him."

"If he dies, I'll never forgive myself," blurted Bugs. "I shouldn't have waited for the police. I should have taken the law into my own hands."

"If you take anything, like one step closer, I'll knock you from under your dandruff," snapped Sally.

"You talk big," sneered Bugs. "But you're not fooling anyone. The heat is finally on *you.*"

"Wrong, Bugs," said Encyclopedia. "I can prove the heat isn't where it should be."

WHAT DID ENCYCLOPEDIA MEAN?

(Turn to page 177 for the solution to "The Case of the Grape Catcher.")

The Case of the Left-Handers Club

Daisy Pender walked into the Brown Detective Agency. Across her T-shirt was printed "Left is Right."

"I'm on my way to the meeting of the Idaville Left-Handers Club," she said. "We're going to name our Left-Hander of the Year and draw up our Bill of Rights . . . er, Lefts."

"I heard you had trouble at the last meeting," said Encyclopedia.

"And how," replied Daisy. "Somebody slipped castor oil into the fruit punch. That's why I'm here. I'm worried."

She pitched a quarter onto the gas can beside Encyclopedia.

"Today's meeting is at the high school cafeteria in half an hour," she said. "I want to hire you to watch things. I'll help, of course. I'm practicing to be a detective myself."

She pointed to Encyclopedia's feet.

135

"You've been on a murder case," she declared. "Your sneakers are covered with blood stains."

The "blood stains" were ketchup drops.

"You're some detective, Daisy," said Encyclopedia with a straight face.

Out by the bikes, Sally whispered, "If she opens her own detective agency, I have the perfect name — Daisy's Disaster."

"She means well," whispered back Encyclopedia.

On the ride to the meeting, Daisy told the detectives about the Left-Handers Club. It had been founded by a group of concerned young men and women.

Members fought for equal opportunity in jobs and in dealing with a right-handed world of pencil sharpeners, auto gear shifts, TV controls, and telephone booths.

"One out of every ten Americans is left-handed," said Daisy. "We won't be left out, left behind, or left over."

"Sounds reasonable," admitted Encyclopedia.

"But someone is trying to break up the club," said Daisy. "I guess we made a lot of enemies because we want to be allowed to shake with our left hands."

Encyclopedia was still thinking that one over when they reached the high school. About sixty men and women were in the cafeteria.

The boy detective posted Sally and Daisy by the side doors.

"What am I looking for?" asked Daisy.

136

"Anything suspicious," answered Encyclopedia. It was the best he could do on an empty stomach.

Happily, the meeting was called to order. Encyclopedia took up a position by the main entrance.

The club members talked over their Bill of Lefts. During the discussion, three young men departed from the room. They went separately, using Daisy's door, and returned separately. None was gone more than a few minutes.

Suddenly Encyclopedia heard police sirens. Officer Feldman entered the cafeteria. He carried a rifle.

"Remain where you are, everyone," he said calmly but firmly. "We got a telephone call that a lion has escaped from the zoo. The caller said he saw the animal enter this building."

Several girls screamed. Encyclopedia hoped the screams would drown out his knees, which were beating out "Jingle Bells."

Officer Feldman said, "The caller wouldn't give his name. So this whole thing might be a false alarm. We're checking the zoo. In the meantime, please stay here and keep cool."

"A lion on the loose, my foot!" said Daisy. "It's just a trick to break up the meeting!"

"Whoever called had to be here in the school," said Sally. "His timing was too perfect. He waited until the meeting started."

"You might be right," said Encyclopedia. "Three

men were out of the room at one time or another. What are their names, Daisy?"

"Joe Evans, who left first. Then Mike Dent, and then Bill Stevens," replied Daisy.

Encyclopedia said, "The door they used leads to the hall with the washrooms—"

"And the public telephone!" exclaimed Sally.

"Each of the three men was alone long enough to make the call," said Encyclopedia.

"Joe Evans is the one," said Daisy. "He's strange. One of his hands is lighter in color than the other."

"Joe plays golf with my father," said Sally. "He wears a glove on his right hand. That's why it's lighter. It's not as sunburned as his left hand."

"Then the one who called must be Mike Dent," said Daisy. "He's real strange, too. One of his ears is lower than the other."

"What?" muttered Sally. She walked past Mike, studying his ears out of the corner of her eye.

"It isn't his ears," she reported. "It's the hair growing down his temples—his sideburns. They're uneven. The left sideburn is longer than the right."

Daisy wasn't discouraged. "Then the caller must be Bill Stevens," she insisted. "He was the last to leave the room. And talk about *strange!* His legs are too long."

Sally circled Bill Stevens, who was talking to Officer Feldman. She returned and said, "His legs aren't too long. His pants are too short. You're some help, Daisy!"

138

Daisy stiffened. "If that's the way you feel, you can solve this case by yourselves. I quit!"

"Phew," said Sally, as Daisy marched off. "Now we can get to work. Only I don't know where to begin."

"Begin with the best suspect," suggested Encyclopedia.

"But which one?" asked Sally. "Do you know?"

"I think so," replied the boy detective.

WHOM DID ENCYCLOPEDIA SUSPECT?

(Turn to page 179 for the solution to "The Case of the Left-Handers Club.")

The Case of the Diving Partner

Otis Dibbs biked up to the Brown Detective Agency. He wore sneakers and a bathing suit, and he was dry all over.

Otis was usually soaking wet. During the summer he dived for golf balls that had been hit into the water hazards on Idaville's two golf courses. He sold the balls to golfers who liked to use old balls near the water.

The work had its dangers. Golfers sometimes mistook him for an alligator. They waited to bop him on the head with a club when he came up for air.

"Golly, Otis," said Encyclopedia. "What are you doing here? You're way off course."

"I want to hire you," said Otis. He placed twenty-five cents on the gasoline can beside the boy detective. "Helga the Horrible—I mean, Helga Smith—is taking over my business."

"That lazy windbag?" exclaimed Sally. "Every night she must dream she found a job. She looks tired even in the morning."

"The only time Helga lifts a finger is when Miss Casey tells her to," said Encyclopedia.

Miss Casey was the manicurist at the Ace Beauty Parlor. She did Helga's nails every week.

"Helga muscled in on my business," said Otis. "I do all the work, but she takes half the money."

"We'll look into it," said Sally. "Where is she?"

"I left her at the sixth hole of the country club half an hour ago," said Otis.

The three children got their bikes. Otis talked about the case as they pedaled to the country club.

Diving for golf balls was hard work, but worth the effort. Golfers always needed cheap balls to use on water holes.

Also, Otis found a lot of clubs, which angry golfers threw into the water. Putters were the most common. But once in a while he found a complete, matched set.

The business of selling the old balls and clubs had been good until last week. Then Helga came by and gave him some advice.

"She slapped me on the back and told me how much better I'd do with her as a partner."

"The slap on the back was to help you swallow what she said," grumbled Sally.

"You know it," agreed Otis. "You've got to get rid of that big do-nothing."

"We'll find a way," promised Encyclopedia. "Don't worry."

But Encyclopedia worried. Helga was seventeen and could have gone to a reform school on a scholarship. She had a grin like a saber-toothed tiger.

At the country club, Otis showed them where to park their bikes. Then they walked quickly to the sixth hole.

Helga was just climbing out of the pond to the right of the fairway. She wore an orange bathing suit and goggles. She waved to Otis and pointed to a sign near the water.

CAUTION: DIVERS AT WORK

"How do you like it?" she called. "It was delivered a few minutes ago. What a work of art! Cost us only twenty dollars, little partner."

Otis gagged. "T-twenty d-dollars?"

Encyclopedia stared at the sign. It looked as if it had been painted on the back of a motorcycle.

"Otis doesn't need a sign," snapped Sally. "And he doesn't need a partner."

"Wrong, my dear," replied Helga. "With both of us diving, we can double our business."

"You haven't dived *once!*" protested Otis. "All you do is lie in the shade and count the balls I bring up. But when I sell them, you grab half the money."

"Temper, temper," Helga warned. She tapped the

142

thick, smooth tips of her fingers together. Then she made a show of examining her manicured nails.

Encyclopedia looked from Helga to the only shaded place near the pond — a clump of six oak trees.

"Helga could have been resting there, waiting for Otis to return," thought the boy detective. "She could have seen us before we saw her. All she would have had to do was slip into the water and pretend she'd been busy diving."

"A business," Helga said, "has to be run with brains. Now, take the sign. Golfers won't mistake us for alligators anymore. That's thinking the Helga Smith way."

"Fore!" a man shouted from the fifth tee. "Fore!"

"Duck!" cried Otis. A ball whizzed past Encyclopedia and splashed into the pond.

"Go get it, partner," commanded Helga.

"Why don't you?" said Sally.

"I'm tired out," Helga answered. "I've been diving for a solid hour." She nodded at a green pail beside Otis's clothes. "Found nine balls and a putter while you were gone."

"I found the putter and those balls this morning!" screamed Otis.

"Are you calling me a liar?" Helga rose slowly to her feet, breathing heavily on her right fist.

Otis retreated five steps, just breathing heavily.

"Nobody calls me a liar," said Helga. "You prove I didn't find those balls, and I'll bow out. You can have the business all to yourself."

"And if he can't prove you lied?" demanded Sally.

Encyclopedia wished Sally hadn't asked the question.

"If he can't," repeated Helga, grinning her saber-toothed-tiger grin. "If he can't, I'll find myself another partner. And I'll flatten this one's nose till it looks like an all-day pizza."

Otis uttered a low moan.

"Encyclopedia," said Sally, "help Otis!"

"You mean prove that Helga didn't dive for those balls?" inquired the boy detective. "That's easy."

WHAT WAS THE PROOF?

(Turn to page 180 for the solution to "The Case of the Diving Partner.")

The Case of the Upside-Down Witness

Elton Fisk hurried into the Brown Detective Agency. He had his feet on the ground.

About this time every summer, Elton usually had his feet stuck in the air. He raised money for the General Hospital by standing on his head all over town. People tossed coins into his cap.

"You know the three men who held up the bank yesterday?" he said. "I saw them. But I forget where."

"You *forget?*" cried Sally. "Elton, you've spent too much time standing on your brains."

"My brains are fine," insisted Elton. "It's just that I didn't know about the holdup until I read the newspaper this morning. What I saw yesterday didn't seem important at the time."

"What *did* you see?" asked Encyclopedia.

"Three men in yellow coveralls ran into a store,"

said Elton. "They didn't have masks. But they were carrying paper bags."

Encyclopedia jumped to his feet. "Three men in masks and yellow coveralls held up the First National Bank yesterday afternoon," he said. "They stuffed the money into paper bags."

"They probably hid the masks as soon as they were away from the bank," said Sally.

"Don't you remember anything about the store they went into?" asked Encyclopedia.

"It was downtown," replied Elton. "And it had a big sign in the window—a white sign with black letters."

"What was written on the sign?" asked Sally.

"A lot of words. But I could read two of them," Elton said proudly.

"What's so great about reading two words?" demanded Sally.

"Look," said Elton, "I was standing on my head. I had to read the sign upside down. And come to think of it, *backward,* too!"

He explained. He had been looking into a large mirror when he saw the robbers enter a store across the street.

"Last week Bugs Meany and his Tigers gave me a hotfoot while I was doing a headstand," he said. "So I set up a large mirror to keep them from sneaking up behind me."

"The store with the sign must be a hideout," put in Encyclopedia thoughtfully.

147

"Finding the store should be a cinch," said Sally. "All we have to do is spot a sign with the two words Elton read."

"I forget what they are," Elton said lamely.

Gloom fell upon the Brown Detective Agency.

Finally Sally said, "Never mind. Some store window has a sign that's wrong. Two words are written upside down and backward."

"That's the answer!" whooped Elton. "Words appearing upside down and backward to someone walking past would look just right if you stood on your head and read them in a mirror."

"The two words were probably stuck in as a stunt to catch the eye," said Sally.

"We're wasting breath talking," said Elton. "We should be looking."

Since Elton could not remember all the streets he'd been on, Encyclopedia decided to comb every one in the downtown area.

The first black-and-white sign they came to was in the window of Slattery's Fish Market on Monroe Street.

CHOICE	COD
	BLUE
Of Any 3 Fish	KING
	DOLPHIN
For the Price of 2	FLOUNDER

"Every word is plain as day," said Sally.

They moved on, looking for a sign with two words upside down and backward. They reached Dwight's Men's Store. A black-and-white sign in the window read:

BARGAINS! BARGAINS!
Everything Must Go
Shirts, Slacks, Suits
Our Loss Is Your Gain

"No luck," said Elton. "I wish I hadn't moved around so much yesterday. I did handstands in dozens of places."

"Don't be discouraged," said Sally cheerfully. "We've lots of streets to check."

For the next two hours they peered at shop windows. First they walked the east-west streets. Then they walked the north-south streets.

They saw no other black-and-white window signs until they arrived at Highland Avenue, the last street.

In the window of Meleger's Furniture Store was the sign:

SUMMER SALE!
Three-Piece Bedroom Set
Only $399

Four doors away, the window of McDuffy's Shoe

Store bore the sign:

PRICES SLASHED!
Up to 50% Off
SAVE SAVE SAVE

"We're out of store windows," said Elton glumly. "We'll never find the store the robbers entered."

"They might have taken the sign down," said Sally. "Encyclopedia, can't you think of something?"

"I've already thought of something," replied the boy detective. "We've been looking at this case in the wrong way. The robbers went into—"

WHICH STORE?

(Turn to page 181 for the solution to "The Case of the Upside-Down Witness.")

The Case of the Marvelous Egg

Chester Jenkins swept past the Brown Detective Agency. He was carrying an egg.

Encyclopedia and Sally glanced questioningly at each other. Chester hurried nowhere except to the refrigerator.

Furthermore, Chester carried food to one place only—his mouth. He was well known as a fork on foot.

"Hey, Chester," Encyclopedia called. "What's the big hurry?"

Chester stopped. "Egg power," he said. "Egg power is going to make us kids independently wealthy. Wilford Wiggins says so."

Wilford Wiggins was a high school dropout and too lazy to scratch. His only exercise was watching monster movies on television and letting his flesh crawl.

He spent most of his waking hours dreaming up

152

get-rich-quick schemes. Encyclopedia had stopped him many times from cheating the children of the neighborhood.

"Wilford has called a secret meeting at the city dump for two o'clock today," said Chester. "He told us kids to bring an egg and all our money. He promised to explain everything."

"Wilford didn't tell me about the secret meeting," said Encyclopedia.

"He must be afraid you'll shoot him down again," said Chester. Suddenly his face clouded. "Say, maybe I'd better hire you to come along—just in case."

"It's nearly two o'clock now," said Sally. "Let's go."

They arrived at the dump as the meeting was starting. Wilford stood on a burnt table. Beside him was a tall boy dressed in a crash helmet, goggles, and a jumpsuit. Strapped to his back was a parachute.

The detectives and Chester moved in quietly. They found places at the rear of the crowd of eager children.

"It's terrible," whispered Chester. "Everyone is money mad—including me."

Wilford raised his hands for quiet.

"I see you've all brought an egg," he said. "Good. Now take a look at your egg. What do you see?"

He let the children stare at their eggs for a moment. Then he said, "Every egg has the same shape—round!"

"You got us out here to say *that?*" shouted Bugs Meany. "If you went completely out of your mind, no one would know the difference."

"Calm down, kiddo," growled Wilford. "I ought to get angry and not allow you in on the big money-making deal I have for all the faithful."

"Well, what egg isn't round?" snarled Bugs.

Wilford chuckled mysteriously. He reached into his pocket and brought out a small box.

"The egg inside this box isn't round," he announced. "It's *square!*"

Gasps rose from the crowd, plus one shout of disbelief. It was Bugs again.

"Man, oh, man!" cried the Tigers' leader. "When you go to the zoo, you must buy two tickets — one to get in and one to get out!"

Wilford ignored the wisecrack. "Think of what eggs shaped like square blocks will mean to America — to the world!" he said.

The children considered the possibilities. Their doubts gradually turned to wonder as they thought about it. What a gift to mankind!

"Square eggs won't roll off the table," offered Charlie Stewart.

"You can slice them and use them on sandwiches and not waste the bread corners," sang Otto Beck.

The children chattered about the possibilities. They saw a fortune at their fingertips.

"Others have made square eggs," admitted Wilford. "But they had to boil the egg, remove the shell, and then squeeze the egg into a square block. That's not what will make us millions. No, siree!"

Wilford threw back his head triumphantly. "I've done it! Me, Wilford Wiggins! I've bred chickens that lay square eggs!"

The youth with the parachute spoke. "You're asking yourselves if a square egg will break too easily. And you want to know why Wilford doesn't show you the egg inside the small box."

"I'll tell you," said Wilford. "I'm a man of my word. I promised the newspaper and television people not to show anyone the world's first square egg before they see it.

"A lot of bigshots are waiting at the airport right now," he went on. "This young man beside me is Buddy Stilwell, a skydiver. He hopes to take off in half an hour. You can see that he's dressed and ready to jump."

Buddy Stilwell said, "I'll drop from twenty thousand feet holding the square egg in my hand. When I parachute to a landing, I'll show the reporters and the cameras the egg—unbroken! The news will flash around the earth. People everywhere will demand strong, square eggs."

"I'm asking you to trust me," said Wilford. "But I can't lie. I spent all my money developing my sensational chickens. I need your dollars to rent the airplane."

"The minute we rent it," said Buddy Stilwell, "that's the minute the egg and I soar into the sky."

"Right," said Wilford. "So I'm offering all my young friends a chance to strike it rich. For five dollars, each of you can buy a share of the biggest opportunity in history."

The children took out their money. They lined up excitedly to buy shares.

"Encyclopedia," said Sally. "You can't let all these kids fall for Wilford's fast talk."

"Fall is the right word," said Encyclopedia.

WHAT WAS WILFORD'S MISTAKE?

(Turn to page 182 for the solution to "The Case of the Marvelous Egg.")

The Case of the Overfed Pigs

Although Lucy Fibbs was only nine, she was already a swimming teacher. She didn't teach children. She taught pigs.

The job was not all glory. Wednesday morning Lucy telephoned Encyclopedia with a weighty problem.

"Someone is secretly fattening my pigs so they'll sink instead of swim," she said.

"Oh, my achin' bacon," thought Encyclopedia. "What next?"

"You've got to find out who is doing it!" exclaimed Lucy.

"I'll be right over," promised Encyclopedia.

He and Sally caught the number 9 bus. They rode to the farming country north of town. Lucy met them at the stop near her house.

"I'll show you around first," she said. "We can start in the pig barn."

Over the barn door was written: "Through These

Doors Pass the Fastest Racing Pigs in the World."

"Pigs are smart," said Lucy, herding four young ones into a chute. "Watch."

She yanked open the starting gate. The four pigs dashed on a four-second sprint to a feed bowl fifty feet away.

"A man in Iowa is planning to hold the first All-Pig Olympics next summer," said Lucy. "I'm going to enter a team."

"Won't these pigs be too big and slow by next summer?" inquired Sally.

"Sure they will," replied Lucy. "I'm just practicing on them — learning how to train for speed. Maybe I'll cut the workouts down to two a day."

"You don't want them to keel over from teaching you," agreed Encyclopedia.

"By next summer, I should have a few sprinters that can go fifty feet in three seconds flat," said Lucy. "That's about equal to a five-minute mile, you know."

"Do you train them to swim at the same time?" asked Sally.

"Golly, no," said Lucy. "The runners are Hampshires. The swimmers are Yorkshire Whites. Come along and you'll see."

She led the detectives to a small swimming pool surrounded by a wire fence. Near the pool several whitish pigs snoozed in the sun.

"You have to start the swimmers when they're two or three days old," she said. "First you teach them to

159

drink milk from a baby bottle. Then you lead them to the water. Soon they dive to get the bottle. In six weeks, splasho! They're swimming."

"Breaststroke or crawl?" asked Encyclopedia.

"Piggypaddle," answered Lucy.

The pigs, the detectives learned, performed four shows daily at Submarine World in nearby Dade Springs. They had a ten-minute act that included perfect "swine" dives.

"My sister Carol dreamed up the act four years ago," said Lucy. "She works with the pigs at the show. I stay here and look after training. I have to have understudies ready to replace overweight swimmers."

"And someone is helping them to gain weight?" said Sally.

"I'm sure of it," said Lucy. "Usually, pigs can perform until they are two years old. At that age, they weigh about a hundred pounds. If they are heavier, they tire in the water. They sink and can drown."

Lucy told the detectives that last month several pigs were found swimming too low in the water. Her sister Carol put them on the scale. They were twenty to thirty pounds overweight!

"They must have been fed on the sly for weeks," said Lucy. "Somebody is trying to put us out of business."

"Why should anyone do that?" asked Sally.

"Jealousy, I guess," said Lucy. "Lots of farmers

would like their pigs to be swimming stars."

"They must hog the show at Submarine World," said Sally.

Encyclopedia winced. Then he said, businesslike, "Where do your swimmers sleep at night?"

"In the rear of the pig barn," answered Lucy. "My sister trucks them back and forth to the show each day."

"The barn isn't very safe," said Sally. "Anyone could sneak in."

"I think someone did last night," replied Lucy.

She explained. Her family had returned from the movies late at night. As they drove up, they spied the kitchen lights on. Then they saw a teen-ager run out the back door.

"We didn't get a good look at him," said Lucy. "He moved too fast."

There was more. Lucy's father later questioned the neighbors. One of them, Mr. Brandt, had seen two cars, one towing the other, not far from Lucy's house.

"That was about half an hour after we returned from the movies," said Lucy. "It was too dark for Mr. Brandt to see the cars clearly."

Lucy had a second clue.

"Dad found a slip of paper on the kitchen floor," she said. "He gave it to the police. It had two words typed on it: *pig iron.*"

"*Pig . . . iron . . .*" Encyclopedia repeated to himself.

To Lucy, he said, "Where are the telephones in your house?"

"There is only one," replied Lucy. "It's in the kitchen."

"Good. It all fits," said Encyclopedia.

"You mean you know who has been fattening Lucy's swimmers?" gasped Sally.

"Not yet," said Encyclopedia. "But the police shouldn't have much difficulty finding out who he is."

WHY WAS ENCYCLOPEDIA SO SURE?

(Turn to page 183 for the solution to "The Case of the Overfed Pigs.")

The Case of the Ball of String

Encyclopedia and Sally visited the Children's Hobby Show at the junior high school two hours before it opened. Cosimo Bender had asked them to hurry over.

Cosimo was waiting by the flagpole. "The show is being set up in the west wing," he told the detectives. "I've entered a ball of string."

"Say that again, please?" requested Sally.

"String," said Cosimo, squaring his shoulders. "My ball is nearly two-and-a-half feet across. It has a good chance of winning the Collecting for Fun prize."

Cosimo explained. The Collecting for Fun category was a new one at the hobby show.

"Nothing entered in Collecting for Fun can be worth trading or selling," he said. "It has to be— well, junk."

"Is Ralph Stockton showing his broken golf tees?" asked Sally.

164

"In sixty-six different colors," said Cosimo. "Bubba Ludwig entered his corks. Jim Sunshine brought his blown light bulbs, no two alike. There are four other great collections, but my ball of string is the favorite."

The children walked into the west wing of the school. In classrooms on both sides of the hall, boys and girls were busy setting up their exhibits.

"I want to hire you," said Cosimo. "I'm worried."

"What about?" asked Encyclopedia.

"Someone is trying to stop me from winning," answered Cosimo. "A rumor is floating around that my string is a fake—that it has a basketball in the center."

"How rotten!" exclaimed Sally.

"My ball is true string, through and through," insisted Cosimo. "Oh, it has a little bit of wrapper twine and some binder twine. And maybe a few acorns, but—"

"Acorns?" repeated Sally.

"I keep the ball in the backyard where I can look at it whenever I want to," said Cosimo. "Squirrels like to sit on it. They can't sit on a two-and-a-half-foot ball of string just anywhere."

The children had come to a large door at the end of the hall. Above the door was a sign: "Room 9— COLLECTING FOR FUN."

The room was small, and crowded with eight tables. Collections of useless objects were spread lovingly upon seven of the tables. The eighth table was bare.

"My ball of string!" wailed Cosimo. "It's been stolen!"

A narrow door stood in the back wall of the room. It led, Encyclopedia discovered, to the grounds behind the school.

The boy detective's brain raced. Whoever stole the ball of string probably took it out the back door. The thief wouldn't have dared to use the large door to the hall. Too many children would have seen him.

Cosimo was in shock. So Encyclopedia sent Sally to search the grounds. Then he examined the room carefully.

The table from which the string had been stolen drew his attention. The top of the table was marked with scratches about half an inch long. He found similar scratches on the floor of the back doorway.

Encyclopedia borrowed a ruler from the office and measured both sets of scratches.

The table had six scratches in a line. The first five were almost exactly $6 \frac{1}{8}$ inches apart. The sixth was $4 \frac{1}{2}$ inches from the scratch before it.

The scratches in the doorway were the same. Only the last scratch, instead of being $4 \frac{1}{2}$ inches from the one before it, was $5 \frac{1}{2}$ inches away.

"So that's it!" murmured the boy detective.

He read the name cards beside each collection. Four of the boys were his friends. The other three— Tom Gelb, John Morgan, and Charles Frost, he had never met.

By now Cosimo had recovered himself. He was

able to tell Encyclopedia a little about each of the three boys. All of them had a hobby beside the one displayed in the Collecting for Fun room.

Tom Gelb was ten. He built model ships. His model of the *Queen Mary* was on exhibit in room 5. He was a good math student.

John Morgan was eleven. He had the best collection of rare money—bills and coins—of any boy in Idaville. He knew everything there was to know about money minted after 1900.

Charles Frost was twelve but looked fourteen. His collection of baseball cards was in room 6. He was not a good student, but he shone at sports and art.

"Do you know who the thief is?" asked Cosimo.

"I have a pretty good idea," said Encyclopedia. "But I must be sure. Here's what I want you to do."

He instructed Cosimo to gather all the boys in the Collecting for Fun group. After asking their help in solving the theft, Cosimo was to mention the lone clue: the scratches spaced $6\frac{1}{8}$ inches apart.

Within half an hour, Cosimo had the boys assembled in room 9. He closed the door.

As Encyclopedia waited in the hall, Sally returned.

"I looked all over the grounds," she said glumly. "I didn't find the ball of string."

A few minutes later Cosimo came out.

"Your plan fell on its face," he said to Encyclopedia. "I spoke about the scratches and pointed out that most of them were $6\frac{1}{8}$ inches apart. But no one had any idea what that meant."

"Perfect," said Encyclopedia. "The thief has to be—"

WHO IS THE THIEF?

(Turn to page 185 for the solution to "The Case of the Ball of String.")

The Case of the Thermos Bottle

On Saturday, Encyclopedia and Sally biked to the elementary school.

The Parent-Teacher Association was holding its summer carnival. Money from the ticket sale would help buy a new air-conditioner for the cafeteria.

The detectives each bought a dozen tickets. They had started down a row of booths when they heard Benny Breslin calling to them.

They turned toward the athletic field. A large crowd had gathered to watch the chicken-flying contest. Benny had emerged from the crowd and was fast approaching them. He had a hen under one arm.

"What happened to the worm race?" Sally asked him.

"It's been dropped," said Benny. "Too many kids stepped on opponents' worms last year."

Encyclopedia remembered. Bugs Meany alone

had stepped on five worms. Bugs had been boiling mad. He had painted a caterpillar to look like a worm. But the day of the race, it turned into a butterfly. His worm, Fast Ernie, finished next to last.

"How are you doing, Benny?" inquired Sally.

"Queen Cluck here is leading," answered Benny, patting his hen. "If she holds form in the finals, I'll win. First prize is two tickets to the Crest Theater."

"Has Bugs entered a hen?" asked Encyclopedia.

"If he has, it's probably a baby eagle with its claws trimmed," said Sally.

As she spoke, Bugs and several of his Tigers came out of the school. Bugs was carrying a large green thermos bottle, the kind Encyclopedia's mother filled with a hot or cold drink and took on picnics.

"I smell a rat," said Sally.

"Uh-uh," said Benny. "Bugs is trying to make up for being such a poor sport last year. He got Adler's Sporting Goods Store to donate a baseball glove. He's holding a drawing for it at noon."

"I don't trust him," insisted Sally. "Bugs stands for everything he thinks you'll fall for."

"He can't pull any tricks today," said Benny. "Too many parents are here."

A whistle blew. Mr. Pardee, a fifth-grade teacher, called for the finalists in the chicken-flying contest.

"Boys and girls," he shouted. "Prepare to start your chickens!"

The detectives wished Benny happy landing. They should have spoken to the hen. Queen Cluck refused to come out of the starting pad, a mailbox.

Benny pleaded. Benny coaxed. Benny poked her gently with a toilet plunger.

After two minutes, Queen Cluck came out— backward. A hen named Juliet won with a flight of 137 feet, 9 inches.

"Maybe I'll win the baseball glove," said Benny glumly.

The detectives followed him to a table near the library door, where Bugs Meany and his Tigers were selling chances. The baseball glove rested on the table beside a can of root beer.

Benny gave Bugs two tickets and received a slip of paper with a number on it. Bugs wrote the same number on a Ping-Pong ball. He dropped the ball into a box made of clear plastic.

Something bothered Encyclopedia. The green thermos bottle stood under Bugs's chair—yet Bugs sipped from the can of root beer.

"I just made it," said Benny to Encyclopedia. He clutched his slip of paper with the number 114 on it. "I bought the last chance."

It was noon and time for the drawing.

Bugs strutted in front of the plastic box. "I've asked Miss Spottswood to blindfold my buddy, Duke Kelly," he announced.

Miss Spottswood, the school nurse, and Duke Kelly made their way through the crowd. Miss Spottswood wrapped a strip of heavy white cloth around Duke's eyes.

"Watch closely, everybody," sang Bugs. "Are you ready, Duke?"

"Ready," replied the blindfolded Duke. He raised both hands to show they were empty.

Bugs was quick to call attention to Duke's short sleeves. "Nothing is up them," he sang. "Duke Kelly is one boy you can trust!"

"Horsefeathers," snorted Sally. "Duke is so crooked he has to screw on his hat."

Miss Spottswood guided Duke's right hand to the box of Ping-Pong balls. He felt around for a full minute.

"Duke is stirring up the balls," Bugs explained to the crowd. "We don't want you to think the winning ball is stuck on top."

Duke suddenly pulled out a ball. Ripping off his blindfold, he held up the ball so everyone could read the number — 81.

"Do you all see it?" screamed Bugs. "Eighty-one! Who's won himself this beautiful major-league baseball glove?"

"Me!" shouted Rick Larsen. He rushed up to Miss Spottswood and showed her his slip with "81" on it. She gave him the baseball glove and shook his hand.

"It's a gyp," exclaimed Sally. "Rick Larsen is Bugs's pal."

Encyclopedia didn't answer. He was staring thoughtfully at the large green thermos bottle under Bugs's chair.

Sally stamped the ground. "Encyclopedia! If you

can't prove the drawing was fixed, Bugs will end up with the baseball glove himself!"

"No, he won't," said Encyclopedia. "He should never have sipped from the can of root beer. He forgot the thermos bottle was in plain view."

WHAT DID ENCYCLOPEDIA MEAN?

(Turn to page 186 for the solution to "The Case of the Thermos Bottle.")

Solution to "The Case of the Giant Mousetrap"

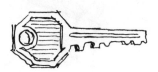

Salvatore was still dizzy when he got into the elevator to go from the lobby to the subbasement. He pushed the wrong button — and got off at the wrong floor.

After hiding the key, he opened the elevator doors again by pushing the "up" button on the wall.

That was Encyclopedia's clue.

The subbasement was the bottom floor, and bottom floors do not have "up" and "down" buttons by the elevators. They have one button only.

Encyclopedia realized that the key was still where Salvatore had hidden it — one floor above, in the basement.

Salvatore drove his machine home, turned it into a corn popper, and sold it to an ice cream parlor.

Solution to "The Case of Bugs Meany, Thinker"

Bugs didn't want to return the cut-glass lamp. So he made up the story about the lamp being broken.

He said he was riding with it in the cargo space of his uncle's truck. Suddenly the truck stopped for a traffic light. That meant the truck was traveling forward.

But Bugs said the lamp "flew back over the tailgate."

When a truck (or any vehicle) comes to a sudden stop, objects inside it are pitched in the same direction in which the truck has been traveling.

So the lamp wouldn't have been thrown "back." It would have been thrown *forward!*

Tripped by his own words, Bugs returned the lamp to Winslow.

Solution to "The Case of the Grape Catcher"

According to Edsel, he'd been tied up in the garden hose for "hours and hours" instead of just a few minutes. He completely forgot that cold water had been passing through the hose and into the swimming pool before he was bound!

Had Edsel been telling the truth, the water standing in the hose would have been warm — having been under the hot sun for "hours and hours."

To prove Edsel lied, Encyclopedia turned on the hose for Officer Carlson. The water that came out had not yet had time to be heated by the sun. It was still cool.

Edsel's parents were informed. They squashed his grape catching for a year.

Solution to "The Case of the Left-Handers Club"

The guilty man was not really a lefty. He simply posed as a lefty in order to join the club and cause trouble.

However, he continued to use his right hand when he was alone—for example, when he *shaved*.

A left-handed man will almost always cut his left sideburn higher (shorter) than his right sideburn when he shaves. A right-handed man will cut his right sideburn higher.

Mike Dent's right sideburn was higher than his left!

The meaning did not escape Encyclopedia. He told the president of the Left-Handers Club. Mike Dent was secretly watched.

Three days later, the right-handed Mike was thrown out of the club.

Solution to "The Case of the Diving Partner"

Helga thought that if Otis, Encyclopedia, and Sally saw her getting out of the pond, they would be fooled. They would believe her lie that she had been in the water for "a solid hour."

However, she overlooked Encyclopedia's sharp eye for clues.

Remember that when she tapped her fingers together, Helga unmindfully called attention to her smooth skin? That was her downfall.

After an hour in the water, the skin would have been wrinkled!

Trapped by her own fingertips, Helga retired from the diving business.

She said the work was too hard.

Solution to "The Case of the Upside-Down Witness"

Elton said he had read two words on a sign in a store window while looking into a mirror and standing on his head. So the detectives looked for a sign with two words written upside down and backward.

They didn't find them.

That made Encyclopedia realize the truth. The two words could be read in the normal way—*and* upside down and backward!

The two words were on the fish store sign. They were CHOICE COD.

Encyclopedia told his father. The fish store was where the holdup was planned, and where the money was hidden. Within two days, the police had rounded up the gang.

Solution to "The Case of the Marvelous Egg"

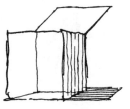

Wilford didn't have a square egg in the small box.

In fact, he didn't have anything. Every word was a lie. He made up the entire story about a square egg.

Still, he might have succeeded in fast-talking the children out of their money. However, he made one mistake. He said that Buddy Stilwell was "dressed and ready to jump."

The children were fooled, but not Encyclopedia. He saw that Buddy wore only one parachute.

A skydiver always jumps with *two* parachutes. The second is used in an emergency.

When Encyclopedia pointed out the mistake, the children left the dump without buying a single share.

Solution to "The Case of the Overfed Pigs"

The teen-ager was named Jim Hearn. He had been secretly fattening Lucy's pigs because he wanted his own pigs to star at Submarine World.

When Lucy's family returned from the movies, he was telephoning his friend to ask for a tow—his car had broken down. In his haste to escape from the house, he had dropped the slip of paper.

On the paper he had typed the telephone number of the place where his friend would be that night. Being careful, he had written the number in letters.

Pig iron on a telephone dial is the same as the number 744-4766, Encyclopedia realized.

The police traced the number. Jim and his friend were arrested.

Solution to "The Case of the Ball of String"

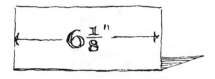

The thief rolled the ball of string out the back door, where he had a wheelbarrow waiting. He didn't want Cosimo to win the Collecting for Fun category.

First, however, he made sure that he could get the ball of string through the narrow door. He measured both the doorway and the ball.

The only measuring unit he had was a dollar. It is 6.14 inches long, but appears as 6 $\frac{1}{8}$ inches on a ruler. Because he didn't have a pencil, he scratched off the widths with a key.

The boy who "knew everything" about money certainly knew what spaces 6 $\frac{1}{8}$ inches apart were — the length of a dollar.

When he pretended not to know, Encyclopedia realized he — John Morgan — was the thief.

As a result, John was forced to withdraw his hobbies from the show. Cosimo's ball of string won the Collecting for Fun prize.

Solution to "The Case of the Thermos Bottle"

Bugs did not use the large thermos bottle. So why had he brought it to the carnival?

Encyclopedia got Miss Spottswood to examine the winning Ping-Pong ball. As he had suspected, the ball was cold.

Bugs had marked the ball at home and put it into the freezer for two hours. He brought it to the carnival in the thermos bottle to keep it cold.

Shortly before noon, he slipped the cold ball into the box with the other balls. Duke Kelly felt around till he found it.

Rick Larsen gave back the glove. Another drawing was held—without Bugs. Benny Breslin won.

ENCYCLOPEDIA BROWN SETS THE PACE

Donald J. Sobol

Interior illustrations
by IB OHLSSON

For Mary Guilbert Brand

THE CASE OF THE SUPERMARKET SHOPPER

IN EVERY CITY AND TOWN ACROSS America, crime was a serious problem. Except in Idaville.

There the forces of law and order were in control. Crooks knew better than to try anything. If they did, they were certain to be caught. No one, child or grownup, got away with breaking the law in Idaville.

How did Idaville do it?

Only three persons knew, and they weren't telling.

Apart from doing in crooks, Idaville was like most seaside towns. It had lovely beaches, three movie theaters, and two delicatessens. It had churches, a synagogue, and four banks.

The chief of police was Mr. Brown. People called him a genius, but he knew better.

True, he was an excellent police chief, and his officers were honest and brave. But the *real* genius behind the town's war on crime was Chief Brown's only child, ten-year-old Encyclopedia—America's Sherlock Holmes in sneakers.

Whenever Chief Brown came up against a mystery he could not solve, he took the proper action. He drove home. At the dinner table, he went over the facts with Encyclopedia. Before dessert, Encyclopedia had the case solved.

Chief Brown wanted the President to proclaim Encyclopedia a national resource. He hated keeping his son undercover. But whom could he tell?

Who would believe him?

Who would believe that the mastermind behind Idaville's amazing police record was still outgrowing his pants?

So Chief Brown said not a word to anyone, and neither, of course, did Mrs. Brown.

For his part, Encyclopedia never mentioned

the help he gave his father. He didn't want to seem better than other fifth graders.

But there was nothing he could do about his nickname. No one except his parents and his teachers called him by his real name, Leroy. Everyone else called him Encyclopedia.

An encyclopedia is a book or set of books filled with facts from *A* to *Z*. So was Encyclopedia's head. He had read more books than anyone in Idaville. His pals claimed he was more fun than a library. They could take him on fishing trips.

At the dinner table Saturday evening, Chief Brown picked at his roast beef. Encyclopedia and his mother waited. They knew the sign. A case had him baffled.

At last Chief Brown put down his fork. "A painting by Ignazio Saracco was stolen Friday night from the home of William Quinn."

Encyclopedia let out a whistle. Ignazio Saracco was a minor fifteenth-century artist. Even so, any painting by him was worth thousands of dollars today.

"Why not go over the case with Leroy, dear?" Mrs. Brown suggested quietly. "He's never failed you."

Chief Brown sighed heavily. "All right, but I don't have a single clue." He put down his fork and told Encyclopedia everything he had learned about the theft of the painting.

Mr. Quinn lived in a small house on Suncrest Drive. The Saracco painting had hung over the fireplace for twenty years. Friday morning Mrs. Quinn had left for Glenn City to visit her mother, leaving Mr. Quinn alone. In the afternoon, he had invited three friends—Edgar Trad, Tom Houser, and Murray Finkelstein—to come over and play checkers.

They played for three hours. Then, at six o'clock, Mr. Quinn called a halt. He had to go to Morey's Supermarket on Clearview Avenue, a five-minute drive away. His wife had asked him to buy four rolls of paper towels before she returned home.

"I've shopped at that supermarket," Mrs. Brown interrupted. "It's so hard to pay, unless you use the speed checkout counter. But then you must have no more than ten purchases."

"I remember your complaining about the crowds," said Chief Brown. "You quit shopping there because the lines at the five regular checkout counters were so long."

"They ought to put in two more speed counters," Mrs. Brown said wistfully.

Chief Brown nodded sympathetically and went on with the case.

Mr. Quinn's three friends had asked him to

buy small items for them while he was at the supermarket. Mr. Finkelstein wanted two loaves of rye bread, Mr. Houser wanted four tubes of Gladbrim toothpaste, and Mr. Trad wanted a brown whisk broom.

Mr. Quinn agreed to shop for them. Since they lived on the same block, it was no bother.

"While he was at the supermarket, one of the three might have sneaked back into the house," said Mrs. Brown.

"Possibly," replied Chief Brown. "The house was empty for an hour. The back door had been forced and the painting was missing when he returned from the supermarket."

"Do his friends have alibis?" Mrs. Brown asked.

"Each of them can account for his time while Mr. Quinn was shopping," answered Chief Brown. "Mr. Finkelstein said he was alone in his garage repairing a rake. Mr. Houser said he was in his backyard tending his flowers. Mr. Trad said he spent about an hour reading in his study. None of them, however, has a witness."

"Then one of them must be the thief," asserted Mrs. Brown. "They were the only ones who knew that Mr. Quinn was at the supermarket!"

"Not so," Chief Brown replied. "Any num-

ber of people may have noticed Mr. Quinn driving from his house. And others who knew him might have seen him at the supermarket."

Chief Brown leaned back in his chair. "Besides," he continued, "Mr. Quinn told me that he greeted two friends by the soup shelves. They were Winnie Dowling, who lives next door, and Clyde Dennison, who lives two blocks away. Put them on the list of suspects."

"But don't forget, dear," said Mrs. Brown, "only Mr. Trad, Mr. Finkelstein, and Mr. Houser knew that Mrs. Quinn was in Glenn City for the day. Only they knew that the house would be empty while Mr. Quinn shopped."

"Not so, again," disagreed Chief Brown. "Mrs. Quinn goes to visit her mother every Friday morning. She always returns about the same hour, ten o'clock at night. I expect many people are familiar with her trips."

"Then anyone in the neighborhood could be the thief," Mrs. Brown said hopelessly.

"And anyone who was in the supermarket Friday evening," added Chief Brown.

Mrs. Brown seemed ready to give up. She looked at Encyclopedia for help. With so little to work on, could he solve the mystery?

The boy detective had closed his eyes. He

always closed his eyes when he did his deepest thinking.

Suddenly his eyes opened. He asked one question. Usually he needed but one question to solve the most puzzling case.

"In what order, Dad, did the three friends ask Mr. Quinn to shop for them at the supermarket?"

Chief Brown drew a small notebook from his breast pocket. He flipped the pages. "Here it is. . . . Mr. Trad asked first, then Mr. Finkelstein, and then Mr. Houser."

Never before had Mrs. Brown appeared disappointed in Encyclopedia's question. She was disappointed now, however.

"How can the order be important, Leroy?" she asked. "You can't accuse one of the three men because he wanted Mr. Quinn to do a bit of shopping for him. Why, I shop for friends frequently."

"But no one robbed our house, Mom," replied Encyclopedia. "The key to the theft of the painting is what Mr. Quinn did at the supermarket."

Chief Brown leaned forward in his chair, suddenly alert and interested.

"Leroy," he said, "if I had a suspect . . . I could put a round-the-clock tail on him. He'd be bound to lead us to the painting sooner or later."

"He wouldn't have had time to sell the painting," said Encyclopedia. "It's probably still in his house."

"For heaven's sake, Leroy, who is it?" exclaimed Mrs. Brown.

Encyclopedia finished buttering a roll. "The house to search belongs to—"

WHO WAS THE THIEF?

(Turn to page 260 for the solution to "The Case of the Supermarket Shopper.")

THE CASE OF THE DINOSAUR HUNTER

THROUGHOUT THE YEAR, ENCYCLO-pedia solved cases for his father at the dinner table. During the summer, he helped the children of the neighborhood, as well.

When school let out, he opened a detective agency in the garage. Every morning he hung out his sign.

BROWN DETECTIVE AGENCY
13 Rover Avenue
Leroy Brown, President
No Case Too Small
25¢ Per Day Plus Expenses

The first customer on Monday was Garth Pouncey. He was seven.

"Have you seen any dinosaurs around here?" he asked.

"Not for sixty-five million years," replied Encyclopedia.

Garth's face fell. "I think Bugs Meany put one over on me," he said.

"Oh, no. Not Bugs again," Encyclopedia said, groaning.

Bugs Meany was the leader of a gang of tough older boys. They called themselves the Tigers. They should have called themselves the Razors. They were always getting into scrapes.

Garth said, "If there are no dinosaurs around, then this dinosaur-hunting license Bugs sold me is as phony as pig feathers."

He handed Encyclopedia an important-looking sheet with a drawing of a Tyranno-saurus and a lot of words.

Encyclopedia read: " 'SPECIAL PERMIT. This license entitles the holder to pursue, shoot, kill, and remove any of the following dino-saurs.' " The dinosaurs that could be hunted lawfully were listed in two columns.

"Bugs said I could hunt one dinosaur from column A and three from column B, unless they were with young," Garth said. "I'd have to clean a dead dinosaur within four days and have it approved by him."

"He told you he was Idaville's game warden for dinosaurs," guessed Encyclopedia.

Garth nodded. "You sure know Bugs."

"I've had to stop his fast deals before," Encyclopedia said. He tapped the sheet. "You can get one of these fun licenses for nothing by writing to a place in Utah."

Garth wailed. "I promised to pay Bugs three dollars for it on Monday!" He laid twenty-five cents on the gasoline can beside the detective. "Can I hire you to get me out of this mess?"

"Tell me how you got into it," Encyclopedia said.

Garth explained. Three hours ago he had biked to Mill Pond to swim. As he crossed the little bridge there, his front wheel struck a rut, and he tumbled against Bugs.

"Bugs's towel dropped into the water, and he got awful mad," Garth said. "So I lent him my towel for the day."

"Nice thinking," approved Encyclopedia.

"Bugs said I was so nice that he'd do me a big favor," said Garth. "He'd sell me a dinosaur-hunting license, and I could pay him on Monday. I grabbed the license and lit out before he changed his mind and pitched me after his towel."

"I'll take the case," Encyclopedia said. "I think I can talk Bugs into forgetting about the three dollars. The license is an out-and-out gyp."

"Get back my towel, too," Garth urged. "I pulled it from the dryer as Mom was unloading the machine this morning. If I tell Mom I lost it, she'll have a fit."

The Tigers' clubhouse was an unused toolshed behind Mr. Sweeney's Auto Body Shop. As Encyclopedia approached with Garth, he saw a towel hanging from a branch near the front door.

"That looks like my towel," Garth said. "What if Bugs won't return it?"

"We'll have to prove it's yours," Encyclopedia replied.

Garth moaned. "How? It's a plain white towel."

Their voices brought Bugs to the door of the clubhouse. "You should wear a hat," he growled at Encyclopedia, "so I know that strange growth on your neck is your head."

The detective was used to Bugs's warm and friendly greetings. "We've come to return your worthless dinosaur-hunting license and get back Garth's towel," he said.

"Take your mouth south," snapped Bugs. "This little kid owes me three dollars. The license doesn't guarantee big game, just the right to hunt. And the towel *stays.*"

Garth bit his thumbnail nervously.

Bugs sneered at him. "I've got a cure for fingernail biters." He held up a fist. "I knock out their teeth."

"Time to leave," whispered Garth. "I'd like to avoid unnecessary surgery."

"Not until Bugs agrees to take back the license and return your towel," insisted Encyclopedia.

"That's *my* towel," Bugs declared. "It fell into Mill Pond this morning, and I hung it out to dry. I never even had a chance to use it."

"Garth bumped your towel into the pond by accident," Encyclopedia said. "A lot of kids must have seen it happen."

Bugs's lips moved in a cocky grin.

Garth said lamely, "No one else was around but two of his Tigers. . . . Wait! There were some soap flakes on top of Mom's dryer. There may be some in the towel!"

Encyclopedia felt the soft, fluffy white towel, searching for soap flakes. There were none.

Bugs's grin widened. "Go on, Mr. Brains,

prove that isn't my towel. I'll take back the hunting license, and he can have the towel. If you can't prove it, I'm going to start dealing out lumps!"

"Save the tough-guy talk, Bugs," Encyclopedia advised. "I can prove you're lying."

HOW?

(Turn to page 261 for the solution to "The Case of the Dinosaur Hunter.")

THE CASE
OF THE
USED
FIRECRACKERS

BUGS MEANY'S HEART BEAT WITH A great desire. It was to get even with Encyclopedia.

Bugs hated being outsmarted all the time. He longed to help the boy detective turn things over in his mind by knocking him head over heels.

But Bugs never threw a punch. Whenever he felt the urge, he remembered Sally Kimball.

Sally was the prettiest girl in the fifth

grade and the best athlete. Moreover, she had proved she could tame the toughest Tiger!

When they had fought last, Sally had put knuckle-dents in Bugs's hide. She had left him lying on his back, stunned and moaning, "Deal the cards."

Since Sally joined the Brown Detective Agency as a junior partner, Bugs had quit trying to rough up Encyclopedia. He continued to plan his revenge, however—on both of them.

"You'd better watch out for Bugs," Encyclopedia warned Sally. "He hates you as much as he hates me."

Sally agreed. "If Bugs were voted the Man of the Hour, we'd still have to watch him every minute."

"Speaking of time, we're due out at the old cattle range in thirty minutes," Encyclopedia said.

As they biked to the range, Encyclopedia spoke about the mysterious telephone call he had received last night.

"The caller said to meet him at the range at ten this morning—by the third telephone pole from the left side of the road," Encyclopedia said. "He hinted that the case was important and he'd pay extra."

"Didn't he say what the case was about?" asked Sally.

"He said he'd tell us when we got there."

"Strange. . . . Did you recognize his voice?"

"No," answered Encyclopedia. "It sounded like he was putting on a fake accent. We'll just have to be careful."

The old cattle range was five hundred acres of unused land. There was nothing on it but a row of telephone poles, trees, underbrush, snakes, and birds.

Encyclopedia and Sally left the paved road. They followed a dirt one that wandered this way and that, its destination lost in the wilderness. After several hundred yards, it turned under the telephone wires.

The detectives leaned their bikes against a palmetto palm. The third telephone pole on their left stood in a small clearing.

"There's no one here," Sally said uneasily.

"Not quite," remarked Encyclopedia. He pointed to the telephone wires. About a dozen small gray birds were perched directly above them.

Sally had stooped over and was picking up something from the ground. "A used firecracker," she said with surprise. She looked around. "The clearing is covered with them."

"There must be a few hundred," Encyclopedia observed.

"Let's go," Sally suggested. "Now."

"Too late," replied Encyclopedia.

A police car was coming down the dirt road. It stopped beside their bikes. After a minute, Officer Friedman got out and walked up to the detectives.

A bush behind Encyclopedia rustled. Bugs Meany came leaping into the clearing. "Did you hear it?" he asked Officer Friedman. "Did you hear it?"

Officer Friedman shot Bugs a questioning glance.

"They exploded a firecracker just as you drove up," cried Bugs. "You must have been giving your position over the radio."

"I was," admitted Officer Friedman. "So I could have missed hearing a firecracker explode."

"What's this all about?" demanded Encyclopedia.

"Oooh, listen to him, will you?" howled Bugs. "Mr. Goody-Good has finally been caught with the goods! He can't lie his way out of this. Him and Miss Muscles have been setting off firecrackers here all summer."

"The station received a call this morning,"

Officer Friedman said. "The complaint was that a boy and girl have been exploding firecrackers here and were planning to do it again at ten o'clock this morning."

Bugs drew himself up straight as an Eagle Scout. "Fireworks are dangerous and against the law," he announced.

Sally whirled on him. "What are *you* doing here?"

"I made the call to the police," Bugs boasted. "Us Tigers uphold the law. Why, one firecracker could set this field blazing. Five hundred acres of natural beauty up in smoke, *pfft!* All because of a couple of smart-aleck lawbreakers."

"That's a lie, you teen-age junk heap!" snapped Sally.

"I've got news for you," snarled Bugs. "If looks were a crime, you'd have been born in prison."

"Don't get smart," Sally retorted. "It will clash with your brains."

"Easy does it, you two," Officer Friedman said. He peered at the litter of burned firecrackers. "I'll have to report this."

Encyclopedia protested. He told Officer Friedman about the telephone call summoning them to the clearing. The policeman con-

tinued writing in his notebook.

"We didn't do anything," insisted Sally. "Bugs is trying to get us into trouble."

"My, how she blabbers on. Pitiful," said Bugs. "Think of the headlines tomorrow: 'Idaville Disgraced—Son of Police Chief and Female Sidekick Nabbed in the Act!'"

Sally's cheeks reddened in helpless rage. She looked up at the birds perched on the telephone wires. "They saw everything. If only birds could talk!"

"They don't have to say a word," remarked Encyclopedia. "As usual, Bugs talked too much."

WHAT WAS BUGS'S MISTAKE?

(Turn to page 262 for the solution to "The Case of the Used Firecrackers.")

THE CASE
OF THE
UGLIEST DOG

ENCYCLOPEDIA AND SALLY REACHED
the high school shortly before the First Annual Idaville Children's Dog Show was to
start.

Little kids and dogs of every description
were gathered at one end of the football
field. Sally stooped to pet a cocker spaniel
wearing sunglasses and a straw hat.

"Hold it!" called Scott Curtis, clicking his
camera.

Scott was the neighborhood shutterbug.

He could make a photograph of a drowning bullfrog look like the centerfold of a dance magazine.

"That was a nifty shot," he said to Sally. "I'm the official show photographer, you know."

"Gosh, Scott, how neat!" Sally exclaimed.

"Thanks," Scott replied. "This is a great day for me and all animal lovers."

"So I see," Encyclopedia commented. "But aren't there an awful lot of strange mutts here?"

"That's the idea," Scott said. "Any dog can be entered. This isn't one of those snobby shows."

"Why the costumes?" asked Sally.

"There's a class for the best-dressed dog," Scott answered. "There are other classes for the funniest dog, the oldest-looking dog, and the ugliest dog. The main event is worst in show."

Scott pointed to Jim Mack and his dog, Twitchy. "Twitchy is the favorite to win ugliest dog," he said.

Encyclopedia could see why. Twitchy looked like a cross between a St. Bernard and a French rat.

"I guess every little kid should be proud of

his pet," Sally said softly.

"Any pet is beautiful," stated Scott. "It's just that some aren't so beautiful on the outside."

He turned to snap a picture of a passing collie in an apron, beads, and wig. Then he waved to the detectives and hurried off to take more pictures.

Encyclopedia and Sally wandered among the dogs. Most of them looked like they had been given a home out of sympathy.

At noon the judging started. For each class there was a champion and ten runners-up. Nearly every kid would win a prize.

Twitchy didn't win anything. When the ugliest-dog contest was called, she was fast asleep and could not be wakened. Unable to make it to the judges' ring, she was disqualified.

Despite the excitement over Twitchy, the show went on.

Kate Felton's pooch, Something Else, won ugliest dog and later worst in show, but only after Kate had convinced the judges that Something Else was a dog, not a dust mop.

After the prizes had been awarded, Scott Curtis collected the champions and runners-up for a group photograph. He asked Kate Felton, the grand winner, to pose in the center

of the front row. She refused.

She had tripped, she said, against the freshly painted side of the gym. The front of her skirt was smeared with dried white paint. "I look awful," she wailed.

The others argued with her in vain. Sally offered to exchange skirts for the picture.

"Oh, no! I can't have my picture taken in your purple polka-dot skirt and my orange blouse," Kate complained. "The colors are gross together."

The other children lost patience.

"Aw, hurry up and change, Kate," screamed Bill Seiple.

"Who'll notice the colors, anyway?" yelled Ted Corbin.

"They won't even show," chimed in Earl Hanes.

"Stop acting like a spoiled brat," scolded Debbie Worthheimer.

"Oh, all right," said Kate, and reluctantly joined the group.

That evening, Sally stayed at Encyclopedia's house for dinner. She was still grumbling about Kate Felton's behavior when the telephone rang. It was Jim Mack, Twitchy's owner.

"My dad took Twitchy to the veterinarian,"

he told Encyclopedia. "Twitchy was drugged!"

Half an hour later Scott Curtis rang the doorbell. "Somebody changed the film in my camera," he said. "The film I just developed has only the four shots I snapped of the winners. It's black and white, and everyone knows I was shooting color."

He explained that he had left his camera in the custodian's office for half an hour while he paraded his dog, Brownie, in the ugliest-dog class. During that time, Mr. Everet, the custodian, had gone outside, leaving the office empty for about ten minutes.

"If someone wanted your film, why didn't he steal the camera?" Sally mused.

"Probably he didn't dare risk being seen with it," said Scott. "But why didn't he just steal the film? Why did he replace it with another roll?"

"Because," said Encyclopedia thoughtfully, "he didn't want you to learn that anything was wrong while he was still at the show."

Sally said, "One thing is certain. The guilty person must be someone who had a camera of his own at the show."

"That's no help," Scott objected. "Almost everyone had a camera. What puzzles me is why anyone wanted *my* film."

"Perhaps you took a picture of something you weren't supposed to," suggested Encyclopedia.

Scott shook his head. "I photographed only dogs and people."

"Kate Felton is the one," declared Sally. "All that fuss about paint on her clothes. Encyclopedia, you should question her!"

"No need to," replied the boy detective. "I already know who drugged Twitchy and stole Scott's film."

WHO?

(Turn to page 263 for the solution to "The Case of the Ugliest Dog.")

THE CASE OF HILBERT'S SONG

ON WEDNESDAY AFTERNOON, ENCY-clopedia and Sally closed the detective agency at one o'clock and headed for Maggie DeLong's birthday party.

At the corner of Bleeker Street, Hilbert Capps joined them without a word.

Hilbert was the state junior hollering champion. Normally he was quick to talk about his hobby. How hollering was a dying art. How hollerers were being replaced by screechers, screamers, and yellers. But not today.

He greeted the detectives with a friendly wave and fell into step beside them. He did not holler a single chorus of "Precious Memories," his medal-winning selection.

"You're unusually quiet, Hilbert," commented Sally after they had walked a block in silence.

"My top notes are shot," said Hilbert in a voice raspy enough to smooth asparagus tips. "I overdid it yesterday."

"You joined a protest march?" inquired Encyclopedia.

"Naw, I shouted down two hound dogs, a garbage-pail lid, and a washboard," replied Hilbert.

He explained. Three days ago, he had passed Maggie DeLong's house and heard some men and women screaming.

"I thought a person was getting murdered," Hilbert said. "Turned out it was just the television. An announcer came on and said, 'You have just heard the top song of the month, "Stompin' in Mother Hubbard's Slippers." ' "

"I'll bet you were glad to learn the screaming was a song and not a murder," Sally said. "It must have eased your mind."

"It *made up* my mind," corrected Hilbert. "Right then I decided to earn some big money. If that was a hit song, I knew I could write a better one and sell it to a record company."

Yesterday, he said, Maggie DeLong had lent him her tape recorder. They set it on a table in her backyard. He brought over his neighbor's two hound dogs, a metal garbage-pail lid, a washboard, and two sticks.

"I beat on the lid and scraped the washboard and hollered at the top of my lungs," Hilbert said. "In no time the dogs started to howl. The more I beat and scraped and hollered, the louder they barked and howled. When the tape was completed, I felt real proud of myself."

"Hoppin' harmonies!" exclaimed Encyclopedia. "You may have the smash tune of the year. What do you call it?"

Hilbert said, " 'I've Been Crying Over You Since You Fell Into the Well.' You'll hear the tape today. Maggie promised to play it at her birthday party."

At Maggie's house, the three children left their gifts on the hall table. Then they joined the other guests in the living room.

After an hour of games, Hilbert's great moment arrived. Maggie clapped her hands for silence.

"I have a surprise," she announced. "Hilbert has recorded an original song. I want to play it for you. It's super!"

The children settled down, uncertain of

what to expect. Maggie went to the back of the house. She was gone several minutes.

When she reappeared, she looked terribly upset. A single tear, running from the outside corner of her eye, glistened on her cheek. She wiped it with a pink handkerchief and blew her nose.

"H-Hilbert!" she gasped, "the tape is missing!"

The children were shocked. Sally was the first to speak. "You probably just misplaced it."

Maggie shook her head. "No, I'm certain I left it on my desk."

"We'll organize a search," Sally said.

While the other children looked about the living room, Encyclopedia, Sally, and Hilbert went with Maggie to her bedroom.

"I put the tape and recorder here," Maggie said, rapping her desk top. "They were here when the first guest arrived."

Sally shooed away Maggie's gray cat, Ladybird, and picked up the empty recorder. "If the thief took only the tape, he must have believed Hilbert's song was very valuable. Who else knew about the song?"

"I didn't tell a soul," Maggie said.

"The only ones I told were my folks and

you and Encyclopedia," Hilbert said.

"The neighbors must have heard us make the recording," Maggie said. "Some of their kids are here at the party."

"You can't accuse them," Hilbert objected. "Everyone in the neighborhood must have heard me and those hound dogs."

"But Charlotte Bevins and Mitch Waller live close enough to have *seen* what you were doing," Sally said.

Hilbert brightened. "We could frisk Charlotte and Mitch," he said. "They haven't had a chance to hide the tape anyplace."

"Wrong," Maggie said glumly. "All the kids went outdoors during the scavenger hunt."

Sally frowned. "Just before I went outside, Mitch passed me. He said he was going to the kitchen to see if your mom needed help."

"Mitch is tone deaf," said Maggie. "He couldn't tell a hit tune from an alarm clock ringing."

"Hang on," Hilbert said. "Charlotte excused herself just before the scavenger hunt. She said she had to fix her hair."

"Charlotte fixes her hair every hour," said Maggie. "To tell the truth, I doubt if either Charlotte or Mitch is the thief. You might as well blame my cat."

Sally grumbled, "We're no place." She turned to Encyclopedia impatiently. "Don't you have *any* idea who stole the tape?"

"Of course I have," answered the detective.

WHO WAS THE THIEF?

(Turn to page 264 for the solution to "The Case of Hilbert's Song.")

THE CASE OF THE CROWING ROOSTER

THURSDAY EVENING ENCYCLOPEDIA was trimming the bushes in front of his house when Lisa Periwinkle raced by on her bicycle.

"What's the hurry, Lisa?" called the detective.

"I'm on my way to make my fortune," Lisa hollered. She skidded to a halt and regarded Encyclopedia with interest. "Aren't you going, too?"

"Where?"

"The city dump," answered Lisa. "Wilford

Wiggins called a meeting there for seven thirty. He has a big deal just for us kids."

"The lazy con artist," mumbled Encyclopedia.

Wilford Wiggins was a high school dropout who began his day by going back to sleep. In the afternoon he figured ways of fast-talking the neighborhood children out of their savings.

"Wilford didn't tell me about the meeting," Encyclopedia observed.

"He's sore at you," Lisa replied. "You always squelch his big money-making deals. Frankly, sometimes I don't trust him myself."

"You can never trust Wilford," Encyclopedia said. "He might be telling the truth."

Lisa's face showed uncertainty. "He promised to make us kids so much money we'd be rolling in it," she said.

"Wilford's an expert in rolling," Encyclopedia said. "He has to stuff his mattress with golf balls to roll out of bed."

"Then come to the dump," Lisa urged. "You might keep me and the other kids from losing our money."

"I suppose I'd better go along," Encyclopedia said. "I'll get my bike. Won't be a second."

It was just seven thirty when they arrived at the city dump. The first shades of sunset were beginning to close in.

Wilford stood facing the crowd of children. Beside him was a youth of about eighteen who wore an overcoat with a bulge in it.

Wilford flung up one hand and then the other, as if to prove he was on the up-and-up.

"Gather round, friends," he called. "That's it, step closer. I don't want you to miss hearing how you can"—he chuckled mysteriously—"feather your nest."

The children murmured with excitement and inched closer. Bugs Meany and two of his Tigers elbowed their way to the front.

Wilford said, "Allow me to introduce my partner, Bill Canfield."

The youth beside Wilford bowed. He drew a rooster from under his overcoat and set it on the ground. Then he took a tiny box from his pocket. The box had two knobs.

Wilford cried, "You're thinking, 'What does this tiny box do?' I'll tell you, my friends. It controls roosters. It's Bill's secret ray!"

"I'll make the rooster crow by sending rays to its brain," Bill announced. He turned the knobs on the tiny box.

The rooster stretched its neck and crowed. It crowed twice more within a minute.

Bill turned the knobs back and tucked the rooster into his overcoat.

"I could make this rooster crow hundreds

of times in an hour," he proclaimed. "But I don't want to wear out the poor bird in a mere demonstration."

Wilford was fairly dancing with glee. "You saw Bill do it! You saw his box send out secret rays that made the rooster crow three times!"

"You're full of baloney," jeered Bugs. "That's a trained rooster."

"You can't *train* a rooster, friend," Wilford asserted. "The rays made him crow."

"So what?" cried Bugs. "What's Bill going to invent next? An electric spoon?"

"Bugs is right," Lisa whispered to Encyclopedia. "What good is a ray that makes a rooster crow?"

"I'm sure Wilford has something else up his sleeve," answered Encyclopedia.

Wilford's eyes were gleaming. He had played his audience to a fine pitch of doubt. Now he was ready to turn the doubt into belief.

"Bill is developing a ray to control hens," he declared. "Hens are smarter than roosters. So the hen ray takes longer to work out."

"Hens don't crow," shouted Lisa. "They cluck."

"How right you are!" Wilford trumpeted. "Hens cluck . . . and they lay eggs. Bill is perfecting a ray to make hens lay eggs on command!"

The children suddenly grew still.

"I'm on the brink of success," Bill declared. "But I've run out of money to complete the research. So my pal Wilford called this meeting to give all his young friends a chance to buy a share of my hen ray. With your help, I'll finish the project, and you'll reap the rewards."

"An ordinary hen lays about three hundred eggs a year," Wilford said. "Using the ray, a person can make a hen lay two or three or even ten times that number!"

The children understood what that would mean. Farmers all over America—all over the world—would buy the ray. Starvation would be a thing of the past. And everyone would make a bundle of money.

"Don't miss out," Wilford called. "Step right up. Buy a share in Bill's invention for only five dollars. A year from now you'll thank me with every breath you take."

"I have ten dollars with me," Lisa said to Encyclopedia. "Should I buy two shares?"

"You'd be buying two shares of nothing," replied the detective.

WHY WASN'T ENCYCLOPEDIA FOOLED?

(Turn to page 265 for the solution to "The Case of the Crowing Rooster.")

THE CASE OF THE BUBBLE GUM SHOOTOUT

ENCYCLOPEDIA AND SALLY WERE strolling through South Park when they chanced upon Cephas Keefer.

Encyclopedia liked Cephas, though the little fourth grader had a temper like gunpowder. When it exploded, he would do battle with anyone. Usually he overmatched himself.

At the moment, Cephas lay all alone in the shade of a banyan tree. He appeared to be giving himself mouth-to-mouth resuscitation.

His cheeks were puffing and unpuffing, his lips were puckering and unpuckering, and he was making noises like a wounded hippopotamus.

"Oh, dear," Sally said anxiously. "I think he's been punched out again." She hurried to Cephas and asked, "Who did it?"

"Nobody," Cephas answered calmly. He puffed a final puff. "I'm just warming up the old lips."

"For what?" inquired Encyclopedia. "To go three rounds with an air hose?"

"Uh-uh," said Cephas. "I've got a bubble gum shootout with Malcolm Nesbit at noon." He glanced at his wristwatch and jumped to his feet. "I better hurry."

A bubble gum shootout did not happen every day in Idaville, and so the detectives went along. Cephas, who strutted with confidence, explained how the shootout had come about.

It had begun a year ago at a baseball game. Cephas and Malcolm were in the outfield. They chased a long fly ball into some bushes and found a beautiful ten-speed bicycle hidden there.

When the two boys were unable to find the owner, they took the bike to the police station. Officer Carlson told them that if no one claimed the bike in a year, it was theirs. The year had ended yesterday, and the bike was still unclaimed.

"I guess I've been bragging too much about what a great bubble gum blower I am," confessed Cephas. "Malcolm said he could pick anyone—even a perfect stranger—and put him against me. That made me boiling mad. I dared him to try."

"If you defeat the stranger, the bike is yours?" asked Sally.

"Yup," Cephas replied. "And if I lose, the bike is Malcolm's. But I'll win. I'm made for bubble gum. I have the lungs of a lion, the tongue of a cobra, and—"

"The temper of a jackass," Sally said. "Be thankful Encyclopedia is here to keep you from being cheated. Malcolm is tricky. He likes to eat his cake and have yours, too."

At the west end of the park, Malcolm was waiting. He greeted Cephas and smiled coolly at the detectives.

"Now I'll choose your opponent from among perfect strangers," he said to Cephas.

He ambled a hundred feet to a brick path and spoke with several passersby. Encyclopedia could not hear what was said. The passersby laughed, shook their heads, and strolled on.

After many minutes, Malcolm brought back

234

a blonde girl of about fifteen.

"Meet our volunteer, Teresa Byrnes," he said.

"This is far out, wild," Teresa said. "I haven't blown bubble gum in years."

She set the brown paper bag she had been carrying carefully on the ground. "My lunch," she remarked offhandedly.

Malcolm handed Cephas and Teresa three pieces of gum each. While he went over the rules, Encyclopedia and Sally edged close to the brown paper bag.

"What's inside?" Sally whispered.

Encyclopedia peered in. "A small jar of peanut butter with a screw-on top," he answered, "and a package of paper napkins."

The shootout consisted of three events. "Whoever wins two is the victor," Malcolm declared. He gave Sally a tape measure and grandly appointed her the judge.

The opening event was to blow a bubble while somersaulting. Cephas went first and blew a four-incher.

Teresa applauded and refused her turn. "No, thanks," she protested with a laugh. "I'd break my neck."

After only one bubble, Cephas was halfway to winning the bicycle!

The second event was to blow two or more bubbles at once. Cephas failed on his first attempt. So did Teresa.

On his second attempt, Cephas got out two small bubbles. Suddenly Teresa was all business. She worked the gum in her mouth deliberately, unhurriedly—and blew three bubbles.

"Wow!" she bellowed. "What luck! What luck!"

It was one victory apiece.

The third and deciding event was blowing for size.

Cephas had lost a little of his confidence. He did not glance at Teresa as he took a deep breath and gathered himself together.

A thin tip of pink appeared between his lips and grew steadily into a bubble. It grew and grew until it hid his face. Gently, as if it were a ball of hammered lace, he pulled the bubble free and held it for Sally to measure. Twelve inches!

"I don't know how I did it," he gasped. "I never blew one that big before, and I had a head wind."

Teresa seemed doomed to defeat. Yet she did not look worried. She chewed her gum slowly and worked it against her front teeth.

She took her time.

The bubble appeared, growing faster than Cephas's had. It seemed ready to burst at any second. Then all at once the huge pink beauty was in her hand.

Sally measured it. Twelve and a half inches!

Malcolm grinned triumphantly at Cephas. "A perfect stranger beat you," he crowed. "The bike is mine."

"It is not," said Encyclopedia. "You cheated."

HOW?

(Turn to page 266 for the solution to "The Case of the Bubble Gum Shootout.")

THE CASE OF THE BOY JUGGLER

EXCITEMENT HAD GRIPPED ENCY-
clopedia's neighborhood for weeks. Talent
scouts for a new television program, *Young
America*, were coming to Idaville to hold
tryouts!

One of Encyclopedia's closest pals, Fangs
Liverright, had been practicing an act in secret. He refused to talk about it. He would
say only that he did "jaw and juggle."

On the great day, Encyclopedia and Sally
went to the civic auditorium to watch Fangs

perform. As they entered the lobby, a tall woman narrowly missed bumping into Sally.

The woman wore a yellow dress and carried a yellow suitcase. She hurried on without a word.

The detectives looked around for Fangs. They found him bending over a water fountain.

"Thanks for coming," he said. "I can use the support."

"We'll clap like a family of seals," Encyclopedia said.

Sally gazed around at the other contestants. "Aren't you a bit young?" she asked Fangs. "Everyone else is a teen-ager."

"I don't expect to win today," Fangs said matter-of-factly. "I'm after experience. I want to go to college free."

"Roll that past us one more time," requested Encyclopedia.

"If I'm satisfied with my juggling today," Fangs said, "I'll work on it during the next seven years so I can get a scholarship."

"Colleges don't give scholarships for *juggling*," Sally protested.

"Boy, are you ever out of it," Fangs said. "These days colleges hand out scholarships for anything."

He lowered his voice. "Wait'll you see my secret act. I juggle three apples and take bites in midair. At the end I'm juggling three apple cores."

"Wow!" cried Encyclopedia. "That's *core*-dination!"

"The hard part is working with objects of unequal weight," Fangs said. "You have to use different force. But having a pair of front teeth like mine is an advantage."

"Switch to candy apples and you'll win a scholarship to Harvard or Yale," Sally said.

"I want to go to Oberlin," stated Fangs.

A man in a white sport jacket came onto the stage. He announced the start of tryouts.

"The acrobats are first," Fangs said. "Then come the dancers and jugglers. I'd better begin loosening up."

He excused himself and went into the cloakroom. The first pair of acrobats had completed their turn when he emerged. He was pale.

"M-my apples are gone," he stammered in disbelief. "I've searched everywhere. Somebody stole them!"

The detectives pressed him for more information. All he could tell them was that he had carried his apples into the auditorium in a small, dusty yellow suitcase that he'd found that morning in the attic. He had put the suitcase on a shelf in the cloakroom twenty minutes ago.

"A woman with a yellow suitcase left as we came into the auditorium," Sally said.

"Did the suitcase have a zipper?" asked Fangs.

Sally thought a moment. "No, it had clasps."

"Then it wasn't mine," Fangs said.

"Can't you get more apples?" inquired Encyclopedia.

"There isn't time," answered Fangs. His expression hardened. "Besides, I'd rather find the dirty thief. And when I do. ..." His lip curled above his powerful front teeth.

"Button up," cautioned Encyclopedia. "How many other jugglers are in the tryouts?"

"Two," answered Fangs. "Archie Longmire and Claire Foss."

"Archie and Claire are afraid Fangs might outclass them," declared Sally. "They have the most to gain if he can't perform. Let's question them."

Encyclopedia was not nearly so eager as Sally to jump into the case. Archie Longmire was a warm and friendly tenth grader who juggled plates. Claire Foss was only thirteen, but she was sturdy, and as warm and friendly as an iceberg kissing an ocean liner. She juggled bowling balls.

Fangs spotted Archie and Claire standing together in a corner of the auditorium. Sally marched straight up to them.

"Fangs came here with his juggling equipment in a suitcase," she said. "Now the suitcase is missing."

"Gee, that's a shame," Archie said. "Will he be able to go on?"

"You know I won't!" blurted Fangs.

"I'm sorry," Archie said. "But I never saw him with a suitcase."

"Me, neither," said Claire. She scowled at Encyclopedia. "Are you *accusing* anyone?"

"No, no, no," replied Encyclopedia as fast as he was able. "We thought you might help us find the thief. Did you notice anyone leaving with a small suitcase?"

"Heck," said Archie. "Kids with suitcases and shopping bags have been coming and going all morning."

"Then we'll have to comb every inch of the building," Encyclopedia said heavily. "The suitcase is old and dusty, and the thief is certain to have left fingerprints."

"Wait a second," said Claire. "Now that I

think about it, I did see someone suspicious. A woman in a bright yellow dress was leaving in one big hurry as you came in. She had a suitcase!"

"I saw her, too," said Archie. "She was in an awful rush. She nearly bumped into Sally. And she had a yellow suitcase like Fangs's."

"That wasn't my suitcase," Fangs said. "Mine has a zipper."

Sally turned to Encyclopedia. "It'll take us a week to search all the rooms in the building," she said. "We're not even sure if the thief hid the suitcase or made off with it."

"Why don't you ask the thief?" suggested Encyclopedia.

WHO WAS THE THIEF?

(Turn to page 267 for the solution to "The Case of the Boy Juggler.")

THE CASE OF THE PRACTICAL JOKERS

SUNDAY ENCYCLOPEDIA AND SALLY took the number 9 bus to the farmlands north of town to visit Lucy Fibbs. Lucy was training her pet hog, Julius Caesar, to be the strongest hog in the world.

As they got off the bus, the detectives saw Julius exercising. Lucy's poodle led the hog by a leash and was setting a fast pace along a cornfield.

"Roadwork builds up Julius's muscles," Lucy said after she had greeted the detectives. "I don't want him to be just bacon."

Sally whistled. "Who'd believe a little dog could run a big hog!"

"I've taught Julius to obey simple commands," Lucy said proudly. "I want him to be smart, too."

The poodle and Julius drew up beside Lucy. She patted both animals and undid the leash.

"Julius is only eight months old," she said. "I'm bringing him along slowly, but already he can pull seven tons."

"Wait till he reaches his full growth," Encyclopedia murmured.

"He'll pull fifteen tons easily," asserted Lucy. "He's tremendous—a once-in-a-lifetime hog."

She led the detectives up the dirt road toward the house. Julius trotted by his pal, the poodle, and oinked contentedly.

Three tall youths were on the side lawn. Encyclopedia recognized them: Conrad Benton, Morris Purvey, and Andrew Wagner. They were sons of neighboring farmers.

Lucy said, "They stop by to check on Julius. But one of them is *too* interested. I think he's the person who tried to steal Julius last night. He was scared off by the poodle's barking."

Suddenly she put a finger to her lips and

whispered, "They love practical jokes. Watch."

Conrad was lying on his back, apparently asleep. Morris was kneeling at Conrad's feet, tying his shoelaces together. Andrew had sneaked up behind Morris.

Andrew struck a match and lighted several other matches that he had planted between the sole and upper part of Morris's shoe. As Morris finished tying Conrad's laces together, the flames burned to the matchheads in his own shoe and flared.

Morris screamed, "Yikes!" and hopped in pain. Conrad, startled, leaped up, tried to take a step, and tumbled over his bound feet. Andrew roared with laughter.

"Morris will have some blister," observed Encyclopedia.

"I don't like practical jokes," Sally said disgustedly.

Morris did a one-legged turkey trot for several minutes before he tried his weight on the wounded foot.

"Why is Andrew's clothing wet?" asked Encyclopedia.

"I'll show you," Lucy answered and took the detectives to the rear of the house. The porch was puddled with water.

"I'm alone in the house today," Lucy said.

"A little while ago, Andrew came into the house and asked for a drink. While he was inside, either Morris or Conrad balanced a plastic bucket of water above the screen door."

"When Andrew came out, *kaplum!*" Sally said.

"He swore he'd get even," Lucy said. "The three boys don't like one another very much."

"What about the attempt to steal Julius last night?" asked Encyclopedia.

"I've laid a trap for the thief," Lucy replied. "I made up a record of Julius's diet in a little black book. This morning, I showed each boy where I keep it."

"Was that wise?" Sally asked.

"The book is a fake," Lucy said. "Julius will eat anything. I just give him a lot of it."

Encyclopedia smiled. "You expect the boy who failed to steal Julius to try to steal the book and develop a Hercules hog of his own."

"When he tries to snatch the book, I'll catch him!" said Lucy.

She walked into the living room to fetch the book and show it to the detectives. It was gone!

"The thief must have sneaked in while I answered the telephone a few minutes before you arrived."

Encyclopedia went looking for clues. On the bare hall floor he found a faint set of wet footprints. They led from the rear door to the carpet of the living room and back.

"Crazy!" exclaimed Sally. "They look like the thief walked in mittens!"

"His socks had holes through which his big toes stuck out," Encyclopedia explained.

"He must have taken off his shoes on the wet porch so as not to make any noise," Lucy said.

"All we have to do is search each boy and find the book and two naked toes," Sally declared.

"Suppose they won't let us?" asked Lucy.

"You're right, they're too big," Sally replied. "So . . . we'll just have to be sure of our man first."

"The thief might be Andrew," Lucy said.

"Right," Sally said. "There's something wrong with his story about getting soaked by the bucket. How did he keep his matches dry enough to give Morris a hot foot?"

"Sorry," Lucy said, "I have to tell you that he borrowed the matches from me *after* he got soaked."

"That makes Morris our man," Sally said, though hesitantly. "Look how quietly he

251

sneaked up on Conrad. He's light-fingered, too. He tied Conrad's shoelaces together without waking him."

"Maybe Conrad wasn't really asleep," Lucy pointed out. "He could have been acting to make us believe he'd been sleeping when the book was stolen."

Sally grunted helplessly. "This case beats me. What do you think, Encyclopedia?"

"I think," said the detective, "that we can safely accuse—"

WHOM?

(Turn to page 268 for the solution to "The Case of the Practical Jokers.")

THE CASE OF THE MARATHON RUNNER

CICERO STURGESS, IDAVILLE'S GREAT-est child actor, staggered into the Brown Detective Agency and fell on his face.

Encyclopedia and Sally rushed to his side. As they stooped to aid him, Cicero jumped up and grinned.

"I fooled you!" he cried.

"You're not hurt?" Sally said. "What's the big idea?"

"The marathon race tomorrow," Cicero answered. "It will launch my stage career nationwide. Think of the publicity! 'Ten-Year-Old Actor Proves His Grit!' "

Sally gasped in astonishment. "You've entered the Idaville marathon?"

"Every step," Cicero replied. "When I collapse at the finish line, I'll be the center of attention."

He went into his finish-line act again, lurching like a man dying of the bends.

"There'll be waves of interviews," he said, straightening. "You know, radio, television, newspapers. I'll feed 'em a few choice lines about the conquest of pain and how I never quit. Then I'll bring up my acting career."

"Why should anyone interview you?" inquired Sally. "How can you hope to win?"

"Who said anything about winning?" asked Cicero.

"Well, what—"

"I've been training for three days," declared Cicero. "Plenty of overeating and no exercise. I'm in shape, and I'm ready. I plan to finish last."

Encyclopedia wished him luck.

"I'll need it," replied Cicero. "Anyone can win a marathon. It isn't so easy to finish last."

With that, he departed the way he had entered, staggering toward an imaginary finish line.

The next day, Sunday, the detectives biked to City Hall, where the marathon was to begin. Cicero, the youngest runner, wore number 84.

At two o'clock, the starter fired his gun. Encyclopedia and Sally watched till the runners were out of sight. Then they peddled to the seven-mile mark of the race.

Nearly two hours later, Cicero jogged by. He was locked in a struggle for last place with a woman wearing a neck brace and a man running backward.

"Keep it up, Cicero!" Sally shouted. To Encyclopedia she said with a sigh, "This may go on all night."

There was nothing to do but telephone their parents and say they would be home late. They went to a movie and ate dinner at Andy's Pizza Parlor.

Night had fallen when they stopped outside the Idaville Concert Hall, a mile from the finish, and cheered a few runners laboring past. Encyclopedia pointed to the large electric sign above the concert hall: "Tonight Only—Railroad Brotherhood Band Concert."

"We might as well go in," he said. "Cicero won't be coming by for another hour."

The detectives bought tickets and forgot about the time as they sat listening to the music. Just before the intermission, the band struck up a medley of state songs.

"This piece sounds like 'I've Been Workin' on the Railroad,' " Sally said. "But the program lists the title as 'Eyes of Texas.' "

"Both songs have the same tune," Encyclopedia explained, glancing down at Sally's program. He noticed her watch. It was nearly nine o'clock!

"We may miss Cicero!" he gasped. "C'mon!"

By taking a shortcut, they reached the finish line of the marathon in three minutes. The area was nearly deserted.

All the spectators had gone home, and the last officials were preparing to leave. The first-aid station had closed. A single reporter chatted idly with men from a television truck as they packed their gear.

Suddenly someone shouted, "Hold everything! Here comes one more!"

A TV man grabbed a camera and aimed it down the shadowed street at a small figure— number 84. It was Cicero! The young actor wobbled like a broken top and fell across the finish line.

"He's done it!" yelled Sally. "He's lost to everyone!"

"He took more than seven hours," marveled Encyclopedia.

Surrounded by a storm of congratulations, Cicero quickly livened to his task. He struck pose after pose, gestured, bowed, and likened the hardships of a marathon to getting ahead in acting.

He was delivering lines from his most recent dramatic appearance when Millicent Potter, number 76, crossed the finish line. All at once, Cicero was without an audience. Everyone dashed to welcome the new loser.

Millicent, a pretty tenth grader, seemed astonished by her sudden importance. She hadn't realized, she said, that she was the only runner still on the course.

"This is my first marathon, and I didn't think I could make it," she said, panting. "Then I passed the concert hall while the Railroad Band was playing 'Eyes of Texas.' The music inspired me."

She wiped her face with a forearm and smiled bravely at the TV camera.

"I started humming as I ran the last mile," she said. "Music gives me strength. Music is my life. I hope to be a singer after I graduate high school. But it's so hard for an unknown to get a break today. . . ."

Cicero was listening to her in shock. She had not only stolen his great moment, she was using it to advance *her* career.

"I feel sorry for Cicero," Sally said. "What tough luck to have outrun Millicent."

"He didn't," replied Encyclopedia. "When the officials learn what Millicent did, they'll declare Cicero the rightful last-place finisher."

WHAT DID ENCYCLOPEDIA MEAN?

(Turn to page 269 for the solution to "The Case of the Marathon Runner.")

Solution
THE CASE
OF THE
SUPERMARKET SHOPPER

Encyclopedia realized the thief was Mr. Houser, who made sure Mr. Quinn was away from his house a good while.

Mr. Quinn had to buy four rolls of paper towels, a whisk broom for Mr. Trad, and two loaves of bread for Mr. Finkelstein. With only seven purchases, Mr. Quinn could use the speed counter, where the limit was ten.

So Mr. Houser asked for four tubes of toothpaste to bring the total to *eleven* purchases. Therefore, Mr. Quinn had to wait in one of the long lines at the regular checkout counters, delaying his return home by fifteen or twenty minutes.

The painting was found hidden in Mr. Houser's attic.

Solution
THE CASE
OF THE
DINOSAUR HUNTER

Bugs said the towel had fallen into Mill Pond and that he had hung it out to dry. Because it was a plain white towel, he didn't think anyone could prove it wasn't his.

Wrong! Encyclopedia could.

The detective *felt* the towel. It was soft and fluffy.

Only a towel that has been machine dried—like Garth's was—will come out soft and fluffy. A towel that has been thoroughly soaked and hung out in the air will feel stiff after it has dried.

Thanks to Encyclopedia, Bugs took back the dinosaur license and returned Garth's towel.

Solution
THE CASE
OF THE
USED FIRECRACKERS

Bugs Meany blamed Encyclopedia and Sally for setting off firecrackers. Actually, he and his Tigers had been setting them off all summer.

Bugs thought he had everything figured out. Officer Friedman naturally would radio his position when he arrived on the scene. So he wouldn't be sure about hearing a firecracker go off, as Bugs said it had.

But Bugs had forgotten about the birds. If the detectives had really set off a firecracker, the noise would have frightened the birds away.

As Encyclopedia pointed out to Officer Friedman, the birds were sitting peacefully on the wires above them.

Solution
THE CASE
OF THE
UGLIEST DOG

Earl Hanes sought to improve his dog's chances of winning the ugliest-dog class.

While pretending to pat Twitchy, Earl secretly fed her sleeping pills. But then he became afraid that Scott Curtis had unknowingly photographed him in the act. So Earl removed the evidence, Scott's color film, and substituted a roll of his own, which was black and white.

Later, Kate Felton didn't wish to pose in her orange blouse and Sally's purple skirt. Impatient with Kate, Earl gave himself away. He shouted that the colors "won't show." Only the person who *knew* Scott had black-and-white film in his camera could have been so certain.

Because of Encyclopedia's keen ear and memory, Earl had to confess.

Solution
THE CASE
OF
HILBERT'S SONG

The thief was Maggie, who pretended to be terribly upset about the disappearance of the tape.

Using an eyedropper, she faked a tear. But she placed the drop of water on the outside corner of her eye. That was her mistake!

If only one tear falls, it will run from the *inside* corner of the eye, by the nose, and not from the *outside* corner.

Encyclopedia spotted the mistake, and Maggie confessed. She had hidden the tape, planning to sell it as her own.

Hilbert sent the tape to a record company. It was returned with a note saying his song had a pretty good beat, but it wasn't loud enough, and it needed more singers.

Solution
THE CASE
OF THE
CROWING ROOSTER

Encyclopedia noticed what the other children had overlooked—what really made the rooster crow. It wasn't the ray.

Bill had kept the rooster hidden under his overcoat, in darkness. When he took it out, the bird saw the first shades of *sunset*. But it thought, after being kept in darkness, that the time of day was *sunrise*.

Hence the rooster did what roosters do naturally at sunrise. It crowed.

Thanks to Encyclopedia, none of the children gave Wilford money for the phony ray.

Solution
THE CASE
OF THE
BUBBLE GUM SHOOTOUT

Teresa wasn't the "perfect stranger" Malcolm made her out to be. She had come *prepared* to blow bubble gum.

Encyclopedia realized immediately that the peanut butter wasn't her lunch, as she pretended. There was nothing to spread it on or eat it with.

What was the peanut butter for? Encyclopedia knew.

Peanut butter is the handiest thing to use for *untangling hair stuck with bubble gum.*

After being faced with the evidence, Malcolm admitted he had cheated. Teresa was his cousin—the under-sixteen girls' bubble gum champion of nearby Glenn City.

Cephas lost the shootout, but he won the bike.

Solution
THE CASE
OF THE
BOY JUGGLER

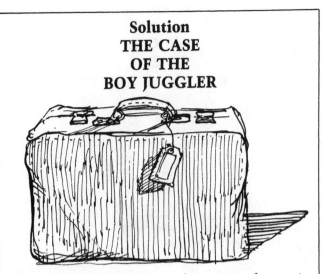

The thief was Archie, who wanted to win the juggling contest.

When Encyclopedia remarked that the thief's fingerprints would be on Fangs's suitcase, Archie became frightened. He tried to cast suspicion on the woman in the yellow dress. He said, ". . . she had a yellow suitcase like Fangs's."

But earlier Archie had said he hadn't seen Fangs's suitcase. So he couldn't have known it was yellow unless he was the thief!

Foiled by his own words, he showed Fangs where he'd hidden the suitcase.

Fangs had just enough time to take the stage. But without a warm-up, he gagged on an apple and had to withdraw.

Solution
THE CASE
OF THE
PRACTICAL JOKERS

Conrad had put the water bucket over the screen door, but Morris was the thief.

Having failed to kidnap Julius the night before, he stole the book. He expected to grow his own super-strong hog by learning what to feed it.

Encyclopedia knew because Morris hopped around "for several minutes" after receiving the "hot foot." An innocent boy would have removed the painfully hot shoe immediately.

Morris was afraid to take off his shoe and show the telltale hole in his sock, Encyclopedia realized.

After Conrad and Andrew threatened to hold him down and search him, Morris confessed.

Solution
THE CASE
OF THE
MARATHON RUNNER

Millicent lied when she said she had "passed the concert hall while the Railroad Band was playing 'Eyes of Texas.' "

She knew the sign out front gave the name of the band. So, running past, she would have assumed the song was "I've Been Workin' on the Railroad."

Only if she had been *inside* the hall and seen the program could she have known the song was "Eyes of Texas." Both songs, as Encyclopedia told Sally, have the same tune!

Thanks to Encyclopedia, the truth came out. She had left the race after two miles and had not come back until the last mile.

Millicent was disqualified. Cicero was declared the official loser.

ENCYCLOPEDIA BROWN TAKES THE CAKE!

by Donald J. Sobol
with Glenn Andrews

Illustrations by
IB OHLSSON

*For Dorothy Markinko
and Julie Fallowfield*

CHAPTER 1

THE CASE OF
THE MISSING
GARLIC BREAD

IDAVILLE looked like any other seashore town its size — on the outside. Inside, it was like no other place in America. For more than a year, no one had gotten away with breaking the law there.

Idaville's chief of police was Mr. Brown. He had a secret. Whenever he or his officers came up against a case too difficult for them, he knew what to do. He went home and talked to his only child, ten-year-old Leroy.

Over dinner, Leroy solved the case for him.

Leroy never spoke a word about the help he gave his father. He didn't want to appear different from other fifthgraders. But there was nothing he could do about his nickname, Encyclopedia.

An encyclopedia is a book or set of books filled with facts from A to Z, just like Encyclopedia's head.

He had read more books than almost anyone, and he never forgot what he read. He was like a bookmobile that runs on peanut butter and jelly sandwiches.

From fall to spring, Encyclopedia helped his father capture crooks. When school let out for the summer, he helped the children of the neighborhood, as well.

Every morning he hung his sign outside the garage.

BROWN DETECTIVE AGENCY
13 ROVER AVENUE
LEROY BROWN, PRESIDENT
No Case Too Small
25¢ Per Day Plus Expenses

One morning in late June, Encyclopedia and Sally Kimball, his partner, were seated in the garage when Josh Whipplewhite entered. Josh wore a mad and hungry look.

"You missed breakfast?" asked Encyclopedia.

"No," grumbled Josh. "Lunch."

"It's only ten o'clock in the morning!" exclaimed Sally. "You must have just flown in from France!"

"Naw, I never left Idaville," Josh replied. "But part of my lunch took off."

He explained. His mother had been fixing the food for his birthday party which was to start at one o'clock. She had made a big loaf of garlic bread and a chocolate cake. She had put them on the windowsill for a minute to get them out of the way.

"The cake and the garlic bread disappeared as if they'd flown — *pffft!*" Josh said. "My party's ruined!"

"You can have a party without garlic bread," Encyclopedia pointed out.

"But not without a birthday cake," declared Sally.

"Uh-uh," corrected Josh. "It's the garlic bread I'll miss. I'd rather have it than cake anytime."

He put a quarter on the gasoline can beside Encyclopedia. "I want to hire you," he said. "Find the thief!"

"Did you see anyone around your house at the time?" asked Encyclopedia.

"Three or four big boys," said Josh. "I didn't pay much attention. But one of them was called Bugs."

"Bugs — Bugs Meany!" cried Sally. "I knew it."

Bugs was the leader of a gang of tough older boys. They called themselves the Tigers. They should have called themselves the Pretzel Makers. They always tried to make dough the crooked way. The only things they hated more than honesty were soap and water.

Encyclopedia had dealt with Bugs in the past. Almost every week he had to stop the Tigers from cheating the children of the neighborhood.

"I'm pretty sure the Tigers made off with your garlic bread and birthday cake," he said. "Come with us."

The Tigers' clubhouse was an unused toolshed behind Mr. Sweeney's auto body shop. Bugs Meany, Duke Kelly, Spike Larsen, and Rocky Graham were inside, sitting on orange crates and chewing parsley.

Bugs chewed a little faster when he saw Encyclopedia, Sally, and Josh approaching.

"What's this?" he called. "Winter must have come early this year. The nuts are falling out of the trees."

Encyclopedia was used to Bugs's greetings. He ignored the remark.

"This is Josh Whipplewhite," he said. "Earlier this morning you four stole a birthday cake and a loaf of garlic bread from his kitchen windowsill."

"Stole?" exclaimed Bugs. He smote his forehead as if he couldn't believe anyone would accuse him of stealing. "We've been right here in the clubhouse all morning eating rabbit food. Got to get our vitamins."

"You unwashed ape," said Sally. "You're lying."

Bugs tilted his nose. "What makes you so sure, Miss Smarty?"

"Your lips are moving," snapped Sally.

Bugs grew red. "You prove I'm not honest in word and deed, and us Tigers will buy this little whipple-dipple kid another cake and a loaf of garlic bread."

"Agreed," said Encyclopedia quickly. He moved off to the side and powwowed with Sally and Josh.

"All we have to do is sniff their breath," whispered Josh. "Garlic leaves a terrible smell."

"They thought of that," Sally said. "They're chewing parsley on purpose. Parsley will sweeten even a camel's breath."

"Well, somebody ought to take a whiff just the same," Josh said. "But not me. It's my tenth birthday, and I want to live to be eleven."

Sally looked at Encyclopedia. The boy detective looked away. He had no desire to have his nose bitten by an angry Tiger.

"Boys," Sally said disgustedly. "All right, *I'll* do it."

She marched up to Bugs. "Open your mouth if you dare, you runaway from a bathtub."

Bugs seemed to be waiting for the command. He opened his mouth willingly.

Sally put her nose close. She did the same with Duke, Spike, and Rocky. They breathed heavily into her face and grinned.

She returned to Encyclopedia and Josh, defeated.

"The parsley got rid of the evidence, darn it," she said. "Bugs's breath is better than usual."

"There goes my lunch party," groaned Josh.

"Not yet," said Encyclopedia. "I think I can prove the Tigers stole the garlic bread and birthday cake."

HOW?

(Turn to page 386 for the solution to The Case of the Missing Garlic Bread.)

CHAPTER 2

KITCHEN BASICS

JOSH Whipplewhite took Encyclopedia and Sally home with him. Excitedly he told his mother how the detectives had bested the Tigers.

Mrs. Whipplewhite looked amazed. She looked more amazed after counting the money that the Tigers had given Josh.

"There is just enough to buy ingredients for more garlic bread and another birthday cake," she said.

She turned to America's Sherlock Holmes in sneakers. "You must be as good as Josh has been telling me," she said. "But I don't understand about the Tigers. Why did they pay for what they stole? They're big and strong. They could have chased you away."

"They know better," Josh said, beaming. "Bugs Meany has tried his bullying act several times. Sally squashed him flatter than a prune Danish every time they fought."

Josh wasn't fibbing. Sally was the best athlete in the fifth grade. And she was the only one, boy or girl, under twelve who could punch out Bugs Meany. Whenever they had tangled, Bugs had ended on the ground mumbling,

"Deal the cards," or some other line from dreamland.

"You two are quite a team," Mrs. Whipplewhite said to the detectives. She brought out milk and oatmeal cookies and placed them on the kitchen table. "Perhaps you'd like to help make Josh another birthday cake and garlic bread. You could —"

"Mom," Josh broke in. "They're detectives. They have a business to run."

"Oh, but we'd like to help," said Encyclopedia, who was always eager to learn. "Besides, business will be slow for a few days. Whenever Bugs is caught at some mischief, he lies low for a spell."

"And with the Fourth of July approaching, a lot of kids have left the neighborhood," Sally put in. "We could go without a customer for days."

"Then perhaps you'd like to help make the food for the party?" Mrs. Whipplewhite asked.

"That'd be neat!" exclaimed Encyclopedia.

Mrs. Whipplewhite got out a red crayon and a sheet of paper. "If we're going to do a lot of cooking, we'd better have some rules," she advised. She made up a sign and tacked it onto the kitchen bulletin board. It read:

1. Always wear oven mitts when you are putting things into and taking them out of the oven. Ask for help if you need it.

2. Handles on all pots have to be turned toward the back of the stove so nothing will be knocked over.

3. Plan ahead. Read the recipe all the way through before you start. Get things ready.

4. *The main rule*: Clean up as you go.

Mrs. Whipplewhite taught all the children how to use knives and a swivel-bladed vegetable peeler. Here's what she told them:

Work away from yourself

Keep fingers away from knife

Always use a cutting board

• Always work away from yourself and make sure your fingers aren't where they might be cut.

• Use sharp knives. (They're much safer than dull ones.)

• Always use a cutting board. (Never cut on the counter!)

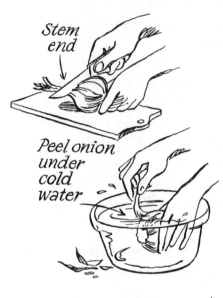

Stem end

Peel onion under cold water

To peel onions:

Cut off the stem end. Now, working under cold water, pull off the skin. (This method keeps you from crying when you work with onions.)

To peel potatoes, carrots, cucumbers, etc.:

Hold the vegetable near its top while you use a swivel-bladed vegetable peeler in your other hand to peel the bottom half of the vegetable, working away from you. Now turn the vegetable around and peel the other half. Be extra careful that your fingers aren't down so far that they'll be peeled instead of the vegetable. In the case of carrots and cucumbers, cut a thin slice off each end before beginning to peel.

Swiwel-blade vegetable knife

Blade moves as it peels vegetables.

To mince, dice, or chop onions:

Start with peeled, halved onions, placed cut side down on

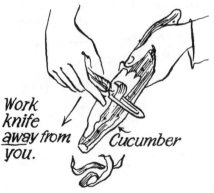

Work knife away from you.

Cucumber

282

a cutting board. Cutting from the stem end up toward the root, make a number of cuts up to, but not through, the root end. For minced onions, which are the smallest pieces, make many cuts, close to each other. The wider the space between cuts, the bigger the pieces will be. (Diced onions are in bigger pieces than minced; chopped are bigger still.) Now cut across the onion, just as though you were slicing it. Once more, the closer your cuts are to each other, the smaller the pieces will be. When you're finished, you will have a little piece of root end left, which you don't use.

To slice vegetables:

For onions and potatoes, the main thing is to have them lie flat while you work on them, which means they should be cut in half. Cut onions from the stem end right through the root end. Cut po-

First place the onion flat-side down and make cuts up to, but not through, the root end.

Root end

Then cut straight across

Cut onion right through root end.

Then place onion flat-side down and cut across

Root end

Cut potatoes lengthwise

283

Hold several carrots together and slice straight across.

tatoes lengthwise. Place the vegetable halves flat side down on the cutting board. Slice whatever size pieces you want by cutting across. To slice carrots, hold several of them together, pressing them down on the cutting board, and then cut across.

To preheat ovens:

To preheat means to turn the oven on, set at the temperature given, and allow at least 20 minutes for it to reach the proper temperature. In some ovens, a light will go out to show you when the temperature is right.

To grease pans for baking:

To grease a baking pan or cookie sheet, put about one tablespoon of butter or margarine on a piece of waxed paper or a paper towel and rub the butter or margarine all over the bottom and sides of the pan until they are well coated.

CHAPTER 3

THE CASE OF
THE FOURTH OF JULY
ARTIST

ALTHOUGH Chester Jenkins could outeat a hippopotamus, he was always neat and clean. His mouth had been his target for so long that he never missed.

When he came into the Brown Detective Agency, however, his mouth was filled with words only.

"The Fourth of July is tomorrow," he said. "We ought to celebrate."

"I know your idea of celebrating," Sally said. "Food, food, and more food. Okay, let's have a party."

"With lots to eat?" Chester asked eagerly.

"With all the food you can stuff down," Encyclopedia assured him, "and enough left over for the rest of us."

The detectives called all their friends who hadn't gone out of town for the summer. Everyone thought the party was a great idea.

The children chipped in and bought the ingredients they would need. Mrs. Brown allowed them to store everything in her kitchen. She promised to let them use her best recipes and to help with any problems.

The next morning almost every child in Idaville and

most of the grown-ups went downtown to watch the big Fourth of July parade. There were three brass bands, a bagpipe band, a drum and bugle corps, and floats of all kinds.

Encyclopedia and Sally stood on the curb and applauded. They were cheering the new Miss Idaville, who was going by on a float with the mayor, when Chester rushed up.

"Come quick!" he blurted. "It's the chance of a lifetime!"

"Did a hamburger truck overturn?" Sally inquired.

"No, Wilford Wiggins passed the word," Chester answered. "He's holding a secret meeting behind Turner's Drugstore in ten minutes — just for kids. No grown-ups allowed!"

Encyclopedia crinkled his nose. Wilford Wiggins was a high school dropout and as hardworking as a flat tire. He spent his time dreaming up ways to get rich quick by cheating the children of the neighborhood.

"Wilford would try to sell electric forks to people on a hunger strike," Encyclopedia said.

"Today is different," Chester insisted. "I tell you, it's the chance of a lifetime!"

"The chance of Wilford's lifetime, you mean," Sally said. "He's never had so many kids to cheat. What's he selling?"

"He's going to raffle off a picture of the Liberty Bell that was painted on July 4, 1776," Chester replied. "The painting must be worth a fortune, but for us little kids, the tickets are only two dollars each."

"Two dollars? I think we'd better go to Wilford's art show," Encyclopedia said grimly.

When the detectives and Chester reached the alley behind Turner's Drugstore, dozens of children were already there. Wilford stood on a stepladder. He clutched a framed painting of the Liberty Bell.

"Here it is, my friends," he called out. "For only two dollars you can have a chance to win this magnificent, historical work of art."

He raised the painting above his head so that everyone could see it.

"My ancestor, Nathaniel Tarbox Wiggins, painted it on the very day our country was born," Wilford bellowed. "See, there's the date, right below the artist's signature in the corner."

Encyclopedia was standing too far back to see the details. But knowing Wilford, he had no doubt that the date, July 4, 1776, and the signature, Nathaniel Tarbox Wiggins, were on the painting.

Suddenly, Bugs Meany pushed and elbowed his way to the front.

"I was in Philadelphia last year and saw the Liberty Bell in person," Bugs said. "It has a crack in it. So quit playing your tonsils. That picture is a fake!"

"Now what have we here?" exclaimed Wilford. "A student of history? Step forward, friend, and take a closer look."

Bugs sneered and moved nearer the painting. He stared. His face reddened.

"I see the crack," he admitted sheepishly.

288

He dug into his pocket for two dollars with which to buy a raffle ticket. Several children started forming a line behind him.

The others in the crowd chattered excitedly. A picture that old had to be worth more than two dollars. It might even be worth hundreds — no, *thousands* — of dollars!

Sally looked concerned. "I just hate to see Wilford rake in two dollars from every kid here," she said to Encyclopedia. "Could the painting be the real thing?"

Encyclopedia didn't answer. It was time to act.

"Hold on, Wilford," he shouted. "When did this ancestor of yours die?"

Wilford hesitated. He hadn't noticed the detective in the crowd. He took a moment to put on a confident air.

"If you must know, Nathaniel Tarbox Wiggins lived to the ripe old age of eighty-seven. You can look it up," he said. "He didn't die until the year — let me see — 1822. So what?"

"So he didn't paint that picture on July 4, 1776, retorted Encyclopedia. "What's more, he didn't paint it at all."

WHY WAS ENCYCLOPEDIA SO CERTAIN?

(Turn to page 387 for the solution to
The Case of the Fourth of July Artist.)

289

CHAPTER 4

THE
FOURTH OF JULY
PARTY

CHESTER Jenkins was impatient. "Let's get started cooking the food for our party," he urged.

"Golly," Sally said. "I almost forgot."

"I never forgot for a minute!" Chester said.

Chester took his appetite straight to the Brown kitchen. Encyclopedia, Sally, and the friends they had invited for the Fourth of July party had trouble keeping up with him.

Mrs. Brown settled Chester down. She assured him that she would help with the cooking. All the food would turn out just right.

With that, Chester became her number one assistant. He followed instructions faithfully and never stole a taste ahead of time.

For Encyclopedia, working in his kitchen had meant lending a hand with the dishes. He had never tried making anything harder than a sandwich, usually peanut butter and jelly. Real cooking, he was discovering, was fun.

Here's what he and his friends had:

Oven-Fried Chicken
Tomato Salad with Snappy Dressing
Potato Salad
Pickled Beets

Red, White, and Blue Shortcake

All recipes serve 6.

OVEN-FRIED CHICKEN

2 chickens, each weighing about 2½ pounds,
   cut up
8 tablespoons butter or margarine, at room
   temperature
½ cup flour
1 teaspoon seasoned salt
1 teaspoon regular salt
1 teaspoon paprika

You will need:
   paper towels
   paper bag
   baking pan(s)

1. Preheat oven to 350°F.

2. Dry chicken pieces thoroughly with a paper towel. Pull off any big pieces of fat. Rub the butter or margarine all over the chicken pieces.

3. Mix the flour, both salts, and paprika in a paper bag. Shake the chicken in this, two or three pieces at a time, until thoroughly coated. Put the pieces, skin side up, on a big, lightly greased baking pan. The pieces shouldn't touch each other. (Use two baking pans if you have to.)

4. Bake at 350°F for 25 minutes, then turn heat up to 400°F and bake 15 minutes more, or until chicken is nice and brown.

TOMATO SALAD WITH SNAPPY DRESSING

Lettuce leaves
4 big, beautiful, ripe tomatoes, at room temperature
Snappy Salad Dressing (see below)

You will need:
large platter or individual salad plates
small bowl

1. Wash lettuce leaves in cold water. Dry. Tear into bite-sized pieces. Use to line a large platter or 6 salad plates.

2. Slice tomatoes into rings about ¼ inch thick. Arrange them on top of lettuce. (Don't use the slices from the top and bottom of each tomato.)

3. Make Snappy Salad Dressing:

1 tablespoon vinegar
¼ teaspoon salt
½ teaspoon prepared mustard
½ teaspoon light brown sugar
3 tablespoons salad oil

Mix the vinegar, salt, mustard, and light brown sugar together in a small bowl, then stir in the salad oil.

4. Spoon the dressing slowly onto the tomatoes.

If Chester — or anyone else with a really big appetite — is coming to your party, you'd better use six tomatoes instead of four. The salad dressing will be enough for either amount.

293

POTATO SALAD

6 medium-sized boiled potatoes
4 hard-boiled eggs
½ cup mayonnaise
¼ cup minced onion (or 2 tablespoons
  instant onion mixed with 2 tablespoons water)
2 stalks celery, thinly sliced
½ cup sweet pickle relish
2 tablespoons cider vinegar
1½ teaspoons salt
Lettuce leaves, washed in cold water, then dried

You will need:
  large pot
  egg slicer (optional)
  slotted spoon
  large bowl
  salad bowl or platter

1. Peel potatoes and cut them into little squares. (If you don't have boiled potatoes on hand, wash your raw ones and cook them in a pot of water with a teaspoon of salt for about 25 minutes, or until you can stick a fork all the way through them. Remove from water very carefully — it's a good idea to have a grown-up help with this — and let them cool.)

2. Peel eggs. Cut them in little pieces. If you have an egg slicer, you can put them through it, first one way, then the other. (No cooked eggs in the refrigerator? Then put

eggs in a pot with enough cold water to cover them. Add a tablespoon of vinegar. Bring water to a boil, then turn down heat and cook slowly for ten minutes. Move eggs carefully with a slotted spoon to a bowl full of cold water.)

3. Mix all the other ingredients except the lettuce together in a mixing bowl. Stir in the potato and egg pieces. Keep in refrigerator until you're ready to eat.

4. To serve, line a salad bowl or platter with the lettuce leaves. Top with the potato salad.

PICKLED BEETS

2 1-pound cans sliced beets
¼ cup honey
⅓ cup cider vinegar

You will need:
saucepan
bowl

1. Open the cans. Drain the juice into a saucepan. Put the beets into a bowl.

2. Add the honey and vinegar to the beet juice in the saucepan. Bring the mixture just to a boil, then turn the heat down and simmer for 10 minutes.

3. Pour the beet juice liquid over the beets in their bowl. When the liquid is cool, cover the bowl and put it in the refrigerator to chill for at least 2 hours.

RED, WHITE, AND BLUE SHORTCAKE

1. First, make the biscuits (you can do this an hour or two ahead).

    2 cups unsifted flour
    1 tablespoon double-acting baking powder
    ⅛ teaspoon salt
    1 tablespoon sugar
    1 cup (1 8-ounce carton) heavy cream

You will need:
    mixing bowl
    rolling pin
    3-inch round cookie cutter
    baking sheet

Preheat oven to 450°F. Mix the dry ingredients in a bowl. Now, using a fork, gently stir in the heavy cream. Mix only until the dry ingredients are moistened. Turn the dough out onto a floured surface. Flour your hands, too. Then pat the dough together until it is smooth. Using a floured rolling pin, gently roll the dough out ½ inch thick. Cut out six big biscuits with a floured 3" cutter. You may have to re-roll the dough.

Place on an ungreased baking sheet. Bake for 10–15 minutes or until the biscuits have risen and are light brown.

When they have cooled enough to handle, cut them in half through the middle so that each half is a big circle. Put them back together, and just let them sit until you need them.

2. Get the red, white, and blue topping ready (start this when you put the biscuits in the oven).

1 pint strawberries, or 1 12-ounce box frozen sliced strawberries

1 pint whole blueberries, fresh or frozen

6 to 8 tablespoons sugar (see below)

1 cup heavy cream or 1 can instant whipped-cream topping

If you use fresh strawberries, wash them, remove the green part, and cut them into thin slices. Put them in a bowl with 3 tablespoons of sugar and stir. Put blueberries in another bowl with 3 tablespoons of sugar. Mash them a little with a fork. If you use cream, beat it with 2 tablespoons of sugar with an electric mixer, an egg beater, or a whisk until it's light and fluffy. Put everything in the refrigerator.

3. When you're ready to serve, put one biscuit on each plate. Put some strawberries and blueberries on the bottom half of each biscuit, then put the biscuit tops back on. Now put on the red, white, and blue topping: a stripe of strawberries on the left, a stripe of blueberries on the right, and whipped cream down the middle.

CHAPTER 5

THE CASE OF
THE OVEN MITT

ON the day Bella Feinfinger began working part-time in her father's kitchenware shop, Encyclopedia and Sally dropped by to wish her well.

Bella was alone in the store except for one customer, Hermes Jones. He was examining oven mitts, which Bella had piled upon the counter.

"I'm looking for a wedding anniversary gift for my mom," Hermes told the detectives. "I bought my dad bookends yesterday. Do you think my mom would like one of these oven mitts?"

"I'm sure she would," Sally said. "They're all lovely."

"So are the spoon rests and the toaster covers," Hermes said. "I can't decide."

Bella rolled her eyes at the detectives. Obviously, Hermes had been trying to make up his mind for some time.

The detectives didn't want to confuse Hermes any further by offering suggestions. So they simply wished Bella good luck with her job and headed for the door.

"I'll see you at my birthday party Saturday?" Hermes called.

"We'll be there," Encyclopedia said. He was glad that kids don't have to decide when to have birthdays. Otherwise, Hermes would still be three years old.

Saturday arrived on time, but the detectives were late reaching Hermes's house. Most of the other guests — Nancy Frumm, Pablo Pizarro, Chips Davis, Charlie Stewart, and Magnolia Peabody — were already in the living room. Only Bella Feinfinger was missing.

"Gee, thanks," Hermes said as the detectives handed him their presents. He laid them at his place on the dining room table.

"C'mon and join the gang," he said, leading the detectives into the living room.

Encyclopedia recalled Hermes's problems at the kitchenware store.

"Did you get your mother's gift?" he asked.

"Yep, and it's beautiful," Hermes replied.

"What is it?" inquired Magnolia, who was inclined to be nosy.

"It's a secret," Hermes replied.

"Aw, tell us," Pablo urged.

"Yes, what did you get her?" Nancy pleaded.

"You're among friends," Chips said. "Tell us."

"We'll keep your secret," Charlie assured him.

"An oven mitt," Hermes whispered, reluctantly but proudly. "It's on the top shelf in my closet if you want a peek. My folks' anniversary is Tuesday."

Chips and Pablo weren't interested in looking at an oven mitt. But Magnolia started up the stairs. She got Nancy to go with her.

Just then the doorbell rang.

It was Bella Feinfinger. Her eyes were red, as if from crying. In her fist she clutched a crumpled handkerchief.

She gave Hermes her gift and blurted, "I must speak with Encyclopedia and Sally."

Hermes nodded and led her and the detectives into the sun parlor. So they could not be overheard, he closed the glass doors.

"Sit down, Bella," Sally said gently. "Now, how can we help you?"

"Somebody robbed the store," she said. "It could only have happened on Wednesday, when I was minding it. Two expensive electric mixers were stolen."

The detectives questioned her quietly. There wasn't much, however, that she could tell them.

The mixers were taken from the storeroom in the rear of the store. Her father had told her always to keep the door leading from the storeroom to the back alley locked. But early that morning she had put out the garbage, and she had forgotten to lock the door on her way back.

"The mixers must have been taken Wednesday," she said. "After I waited on Hermes, I went into the storeroom and found the outside door ajar. My dad didn't discover that the mixers were gone until this morning."

"How can you be so sure that the mixers were taken while you were with Hermes?" Sally asked.

"Because that's the only time the back door was left unlocked," Bella said.

"Has your father punished you?" Encyclopedia asked.

301

"No," Bella said. "He just told me to be more careful in the future."

She broke into sobs. After a minute she wiped her eyes and blew her nose.

"I feel so guilty," she whimpered. "So stupid!"

"You can't be so hard on yourself," Sally said.

"I must find the thief and get back the two mixers," Bella exclaimed. "I must!"

"Strange," Encyclopedia murmured.

"What?" demanded Sally.

"Only two mixers were stolen."

"I don't understand . . ." Sally said.

"If the thief was a grown-up, he would have taken more," Encyclopedia explained. "He would have used a car or a truck to cart off a real load."

Bella looked at Encyclopedia with a ray of hope. "Then you think the thief is a kid?"

"Certainly," said Encyclopedia. "You can't carry much in your arms or on a bicycle. Two mixers are plenty."

"Do you know who it is?" Bella asked.

"Yes, and fortunately the thief is right under this roof — a guest at the party."

"For mercy sakes, Encyclopedia," Sally almost shouted. "Who is it?"

"Why, the thief is . . ."

WHO?

(Turn to page 388 for the solution to
The Case of the Oven Mitt.)

CHAPTER 6

HERMES'S
BIRTHDAY
BRUNCH

THERE was no point in spoiling Hermes's birthday party. So Encyclopedia took Nancy quietly aside. He told her how he knew that she had stolen the two mixers.

Nancy's face went blank. Suddenly tears filled her eyes. "Are you going to call the police?" she whispered fearfully.

"Will you return the two mixers?" asked Encyclopedia.

"Yes," she promised in a small voice.

"Then the case is closed," the detective said.

As if nothing had been said between them, Encyclopedia and Nancy joined in the party fun. It was after the second game of charades that Hermes made his announcement.

"We have something else to celebrate today besides my birthday," he said. "Charlie Stewart's tooth collection was started five years ago today."

Charlie blushed as everyone cheered. His tooth collection was the finest in Idaville. He kept it in a flowered cookie jar.

"We ought to do something special for Charlie's teeth," Encyclopedia suggested.

"We are," Hermes replied. "My birthday brunch will have food that looks like teeth!"

"Ugh," muttered Sally.

"Don't worry," Hermes said. "Some of the food looks like teeth. Some of it will just have a bite in it."

"Oh, is that ever corny!" Sally protested.

"Corn kernels look like teeth," pointed out Encyclopedia.

"Exactly," Hermes said. "We're going to start with corny chowder."

Here is the menu for the double celebration.

Corny Chowder

Toothburger Stew
Cole Slaw
Cucumber Mouthfuls

Tooth Collector's Chocolate Cake
with Tooth Collector's Frosting —
and Teeth

CORNY CHOWDER

3 cans (about 16 ounces each) cream-style corn
1 small can (about 8 ounces) white whole-
    kernel corn, drained
1½ quarts (6 cups) milk
3 tablespoons butter
½ teaspoon salt

You will need:
saucepan

Mix everything together in a saucepan. Cook over low heat, stirring often, just until it steams. Don't let it boil.

Makes 9 large servings. To serve a smaller group of 6, use only:

2 cans cream-style corn
1 small can white whole-kernel corn
4 cups milk
2 tablespoons butter
¼ teaspoon salt

TOOTHBURGER STEW

1½ pounds ground beef
⅓ cup minced onion (or 2½ tablespoons
   instant onion mixed with 2½ tablespoons water)
1½ 8-ounce cans tomato sauce
1 teaspoon salt
1½ cups macaroni, uncooked
3 cups water
1½ tablespoons grated cheese

You will need: large frying pan

1. Brown the ground beef in a large frying pan or saucepan over medium heat, stirring and breaking it up with a fork or wooden spoon as it cooks.

2. Add the onion, tomato sauce, salt, macaroni, and water. Bring to a boil, then lower heat and cook very slowly, uncovered, for 15 minutes, stirring occasionally. You might have to add a little more water, *but* you want most of the liquid to have disappeared by the time you're through.

3. Stir in the grated cheese.

Serves 9. To serve 6, use only:

1 pound ground beef
¼ cup onions (or 2 teaspoons instant onion)
1 can tomato sauce
1 teaspoon salt
1 cup macaroni
2 cups water
1 tablespoon grated cheese

COLE SLAW

1 package (about 1 pound) shredded cabbage
1 cup mayonnaise
2 tablespoons sugar
3 tablespoons vinegar
1 teaspoon mild prepared mustard
1 teaspoon celery seed (optional)

You will need:
2 mixing bowls

Put the shredded cabbage in a bowl. Combine all the other ingredients, then mix with the cabbage. Keep in the refrigerator until you're ready to serve.

Serves 6 to 9.

CUCUMBER MOUTHFULS

You will need:
vegetable peeler

Peel cucumbers with a vegetable peeler. Cut them in half lengthwise, then cut each section into 3 pieces (again cutting lengthwise). The seeds will make each section look like a big mouthful of teeth.

Use 3 cucumbers for 9 people or 2 cucumbers for 6.

TOOTH COLLECTOR'S
CHOCOLATE CAKE

1½ cups milk, lukewarm or at room temperature
1 tablespoon lemon juice
1 teaspoon pure vanilla
½ cup cocoa
2 cups sugar, in 2 parts (see below*)
1 stick (4 ounces) plus 2 tablespoons butter
    or margarine, at room temperature
2 eggs
2 cups plus 2 tablespoons pre-sifted flour
1 teaspoon baking soda
½ teaspoon salt

You will need:
    9-inch angel food cake pan
    electric mixer
    blender (optional)
    toothpick or cake tester
    cooling rack
    serving plate

1. Preheat oven to 350°F. Use the 2 tablespoons of butter or margarine to grease a 9-inch angel food cake pan. Tip the 2 tablespoons of flour around in the pan until it's coated. Combine the milk and lemon juice in a 2-cup or 1-quart measuring cup. Let it sit until clabbered (slightly thickened), then combine ½ cup of it with the vanilla, cocoa, and 1 cup of the sugar*. Mix well. (An electric blender does this job easily.) Set aside for now.

2. Beat the stick of butter until creamy, preferably using an electric mixer, then beat in the other cup of sugar,* adding about ¼ cup at a time. Beat in the eggs, one at a time.

3. Combine the rest of the flour with the baking soda and salt. Beating well each time, add ½ cup of the flour mixture to the butter mixture, then ⅓ of the remaining 1 cup of clabbered milk. Repeat until all of the flour mixture and milk are used, then beat in the cocoa mixture from above.

4. Pour the batter evenly into the prepared pan. Bake for 50 or 60 minutes, or until a toothpick or cake tester stuck into the middle of the cake comes out dry. If the cake's not ready, bake a little longer and test again.

5. Cool on a rack, still in the cake pan, for 30 minutes, or until the pan is cool enough to handle. Run a table knife around the edge where the cake meets the pan and also around the center tube. Now put a serving plate, bottom side up, over the cake pan. Holding on tight, turn the whole thing upside down, so the cake will fall onto the plate. When the cake is completely cool, frost with Tooth Collector's Frosting — and Teeth (see page 38).

This is a very dark cake, almost like a devil's food cake and will stay moist for several days if kept covered.

Serves 6 to 9.

TOOTH COLLECTOR'S FROSTING — AND TEETH

1 12-ounce package semisweet real chocolate bits
1 cup (1 8-ounce carton) sour cream
1 small roll prepared marzipan (you can buy
   7-ounce rolls of this in many supermarkets) or
2 ounces slivered blanched almonds

You will need:
   double boiler

1. Melt the chocolate bits in a double boiler, stirring until they're all melted. Use very low heat. Remove from fire. Stir in the sour cream. Spread the frosting on the cake.

2. If you're using the marzipan, shape into little teeth and decorate the cake with them. If you can't find marzipan, slivered almonds make good teeth, too. Just stick them in all over the frosting.

Bicuspids look like this:

Bicuspid

Molars look like this:

Molar

CHAPTER 7

THE CASE OF
THE OVERSTUFFED
PIÑATA

ENCYCLOPEDIA was walking along Main Street one day early in September when he sighted trouble.

Tim Gomez was standing halfway down the block and looking madder than a flea on a stone dog. He was holding a box and a piece of wrapping paper in one hand, and he was glaring across the street at Bugs Meany.

Bugs was leaning against the wall of the post office and balancing a toy bull in his hand. He was laughing and joking with three of his Tigers—and watching Tim.

"Encyclopedia!" Tim cried. "Am I glad you came along."

"What's going on?" the detective inquired.

"That no-good Bugs stole my bull!" exclaimed Tim.

He explained. His Aunt Maria, who lived on a farm in the western part of the state, had sent him a papier-mâché piñata shaped like a bull. Because there was postage due, he'd had to go to the post office to pick up the package. As he opened it on the sidewalk, Bugs had come by and grabbed the bull.

"Now Bugs says it's his," Tim grumped. "All I have left is the box and the wrapping paper."

311

Encyclopedia tried to catch up. A piñata, he knew, was a decorated figure or jug. In Latin American countries piñatas filled with gifts are hung from the ceiling and broken on holidays. Children, wearing blindfolds, hit them with sticks until they break and the presents fall out.

The detective squinted across the street at the piñata bull Bugs was holding. Except for the horns, which were black, the bull was covered all over with little curls of tissue paper in strips of yellow, orange, and pink.

"I was in Hector's Department Store half an hour ago," the detective said. "I noticed a counter of piñatas — papier-mâché bulls and clay jars — because a lady accidentally knocked a jar and two bulls onto the hard floor. The jar broke, but the bulls just bounced."

"Did the bulls look like mine?" Tim asked anxiously.

"One of them did," replied Encyclopedia. "There were more like yours on the counter."

"Rats," Tim grunted. "Now Bugs can lie his head off. He'll swear that he bought my piñata bull at Hector's."

"And the salespeople will never remember whether he bought one or not," Encyclopedia added.

"Well, mine is different," Tim said. "My aunt always makes a little hole in the piñata and stuffs a lot of candy inside. She stuffs it so full it doesn't rattle."

"That's it!" Encyclopedia remarked. "Bugs won't know about the hole, and so you —"

"No good," Tim broke in. "My aunt seals the hole up so well that you can't see where it is from the outside. I'd have to break open the piñata to prove it."

"Bugs will never let you do that," commented Encyclopedia.

The detective closed his eyes and did some heavy thinking. He thought of how to trap Bugs into admitting he had stolen the bull from Tim.

Suddenly his eyes opened. "Let's have a talk with Bugs," he said, smiling.

As Encyclopedia and Tim started across the street, Bugs took a better grip on the bull.

"Get lost," he growled at the detective, "or I'll pound you so hard on the top of the head you'll have to reach up to pull on your sneakers."

Encyclopedia was quite used to Bugs's welcomes. Calmly he said, "Tim claims you stole that bull from him."

"Man, oh, man!" Bugs wailed. "I'm accused of everything! Listen, I haven't stolen a thing for weeks. I've gone straight."

"You couldn't go straight if you walked a tightrope!" yelped Tim.

Bugs made a fist, but then caught himself. "For your information, I just bought this bull at Hector's Department Store," he said.

"Come on, Bugs, wasn't it quite a while ago that you were at the store?" Encyclopedia said. "And haven't you done some other shopping since then?"

"I don't know what you're getting at," Bugs snapped. "I bought this bull just a few minutes ago. I was heading home when I saw this crazy kid coming out of the post office with nothing but that empty box and the piece of wrapping paper."

"I ought to wrap his head, the big liar!" Tim whispered to Encyclopedia.

314

"Sssh," Encyclopedia whispered back, watching Bugs's fist.

"I guess someone sent him a package with nothing in it," Bugs went on. "When he saw my bull, he pretended it belonged to him. Fat chance. Someone sent him an empty package to match his empty head."

"Are you sure you didn't do anything else after you bought the bull?" Encyclopedia asked.

"I told you once, didn't I?" Bugs's voice had risen shrilly. "What's the matter? Don't you believe the word of an honest boy?"

"Yes, I do," Encyclopedia said. "That's why I believe Tim."

WHAT MADE ENCYCLOPEDIA SO SURE?

(Turn to page 389 for the solution to
The Case of the Overstuffed Piñata.)

CHAPTER 8

A MEXICAN
FIESTA

WHEN Tim called his Aunt Maria to thank her for sending him a piñata, he told her how Encyclopedia had saved his present by solving "The Case of the Overstuffed Piñata."

"I'd like to give your friend a reward," Tim's aunt said.

"Oh, Encyclopedia wouldn't take a reward," Tim answered. "I paid him his regular twenty-five-cent fee."

"I think he'll take this reward," his aunt said. "You just watch the mail for another box — a big one this time. And take it straight over to Encyclopedia's house before that Meany boy has a chance to snatch it."

A few days later, Tim came into the Browns' garage, walking backward and dragging a big box. Encyclopedia and Sally rushed to help him.

"I think this box is really for you, Encyclopedia," Tim said. "My aunt sent it when she heard what you'd done to save my piñata."

"Open it! Open it!" cried Sally.

The first thing inside the box was a note. "This is

an instant party kit," Encyclopedia read. "You can use it for a fiesta to celebrate Mexico's Independence Day."

"Mmm, that's September sixteenth," Sally said.

Encyclopedia nodded and read on. "You can have a tostada or taco party. There's everything here but the food, and I've sent you some easy recipes for that. Have the party outdoors or in a garage because it can get pretty messy."

The first thing to come out of the box was a brightly colored sheet. "Your aunt says to put two card tables together for a serving table and use this for a tablecloth," Encyclopedia said to Tim.

Next, out came six flags. They were green on the left, white in the middle, and red on the right. There was a seal on the white part.

"Mexico's flag," Encyclopedia said. "We can decorate the garage with them for the party."

Then came six big Mexican hats.

"We can do the Mexican hat dance!" Sally cried.

The rest of the box contained paper plates and paper napkins in bright colors; red, white, and green crepe paper for streamers; and a record with Mexican songs.

"Hooray!" Sally called out.

"Viva your Aunt Maria!" said Encyclopedia.

"Olé!" cried Tim.

Tostadas, Taco Shells, or Corn Chips
Refried Beans
Mexican Meat Mixture

Garnishes

Fruit Platter
Polvorones (Mexican Cookies)

All recipes serve 6, unless otherwise stated.

All the food for the main part of the meal is put out on a big table. First, a big plate or platter with the tostadas, taco shells, or corn chips. Next, a bowl or plate with the refried beans, then one with the meat mixture. Now put out all the garnishes, each one in its own little bowl or a small plate. Make sure each bowl or plate has its own spoon for serving.

You can either put the fruit platter and the cookies on the table from the beginning or bring them out later.

TOSTADAS, TACO SHELLS, OR CORN CHIPS

You will need:
frying pan
tongs
paper towels

A tostada is a corn tortilla (pronounced *tore-TEE-yuh*), fried flat and crisp. You pile refried beans, a meat mixture, and whatever garnishes you want on it, and you hold it in your hands to eat it. It's a sort of edible plate.

A taco shell is a fried corn tortilla, too, but it has been folded in half. You fill it and eat it just as you do a tostada.

You will probably be able to buy tostadas or taco shells — fried and ready to use — in a supermarket, a Mexican market, or a Mexican restaurant. If not, many markets sell corn tortillas from which you can make your own tostadas. Just fry the tortillas one by one in a frying pan with about ¼ inch of oil until they are crisp, turning them carefully with tongs. Let them dry on paper towels. (Don't try to make taco shells at home, though. They're too tricky.)

If you can't find a place to buy tostadas, taco shells, or corn tortillas, you can still have a Mexican party. Just use corn chips (sometimes called tortilla chips). The only problem with them is that you have to put a plate under them and eat your meal with a fork.

REFRIED BEANS

You will need:
    canned refried beans:
    frying pan or saucepan
             or
    canned whole beans:
    bowl
    potato masher or fork
    frying pan or saucepan

If you can buy canned refried beans, just put the contents of 2 16-ounce cans into a frying pan or saucepan with 3 tablespoons of salad oil or lard. Warm them up, stirring often, just before you're ready to serve.

If you can't find refried beans, use 2 16-ounce cans of pinto beans or red kidney beans and "refry" them as follows:

1. Drain off most of the liquid from the cans.

2. Put the beans into a bowl. Mash them with a potato masher or a fork. Don't worry if you don't get them absolutely smooth.

3. Put the mashed beans in a frying pan or saucepan with 3 tablespoons of salad oil. Warm them up, stirring often, just before you're ready to serve.

MEXICAN MEAT MIXTURE

1½ pounds ground beef
½ cup chopped onion (or 2 tablespoons
    instant onion mixed with ¼ cup water)
2 tablespoons salad oil or lard
1½ teaspoons chili powder
1 teaspoon salt
½ teaspoon ground cumin (optional)

You will need:
frying pan or saucepan

1. Cook the ground beef and onion in the oil in a frying pan or saucepan, stirring, just until all the meat changes color from pink to light tan.

2. Add the chili powder, salt, and cumin (if you're using it—it doesn't add hotness, but does make things taste very Mexican). Cook and stir for 3 or 4 minutes more.

GARNISHES

Here are the garnishes to put out on your table:

1 cup lettuce, finely cut into shreds
2 tomatoes, chopped (cut them in half and
    scoop out the seeds first)
¾ cup grated cheese
1 cup (8 ounces) sour cream
1 bottle mild Mexican taco sauce or
    American chili sauce

You will need:
> separate bowl or plates and spoons
> for each garnish

Also, if you want, you can put out:

> Minced onions or scallions
> Sliced radishes
> Minced olives, either green or ripe (black)

Put each item in a separate bowl or on a little plate, and give each one its own spoon.

FRUIT PLATTER

You will need:
> platter or bowl

Take a big platter or bowl and pile it full of all the fruits you can find that can be eaten in your hand. Wash all the fruit first. Polish the apples. Rub the fuzz off the peaches under cold water. Arrange the fruit so it will look pretty and you can see some of each kind. Drape clusters of grapes over the top. If you have strawberries, scatter them around the top. Here are some of the fruits you can use:

Apples	Nectarines
Plums	Strawberries
Peaches	Figs
Bananas (in their skins)	Tangerines or tangelos
Navel oranges	Grapes
Apricots	Pears

You might want to try some unusual fruits, too, when they are in season. Some of these are kiwis, mangoes, small papayas, and persimmons. Pomegranates are fun, too—you eat only the seeds, which are delicious.

POLVORONES

(Mexican Cookies—pronounced *pole-vo-RONE-aze*)

   ½ pound (2 sticks) butter, at room temperature
   ½ cup unsifted confectioners' sugar
   2 cups unsifted flour
   ¼ teaspoon salt
   1 teaspoon vanilla
   ½ cup (or more) extra confectioners' sugar

You will need:
   mixing bowls (2)
   electric mixer (optional)
   baking sheet
   cooling rack

1. Put all the ingredients except the extra confectioners' sugar in a bowl, and mix them together thoroughly until they form a big ball. You can do this with a mixer or with your hands. (It's more fun with your hands.)

2. Cover the bowl with foil or plastic wrap. Chill in the refrigerator for at least an hour.

3. Preheat oven to 375°F.

4. Make the dough into 1-inch balls by rolling little pieces of it between the palms of your hands. Place the balls on an ungreased baking sheet. (They can be placed close together, but shouldn't touch each other.)

5. Bake for 15 minutes, or until the cookies are very light brown.

6. Put the extra confectioners' sugar in a small bowl. Roll the baked cookies in this one by one, then put them on a rack to cool. (The cookies should be rolled in the sugar soon after they come out of the oven, but they will be too hot to touch—so pick them up by holding a spoon in each hand, and use these to move the cookies and roll them in the confectioners' sugar.) If you want sweeter cookies, you can roll them in the confectioners' sugar one more time after they're cool.

Makes about 48 cookies.

CHAPTER 9

THE CASE OF
THE MISSING
WATCHGOOSE

ENCYCLOPEDIA was reading about the Roman Empire one Saturday morning in October when Candida Strong telephoned.

"Christopher Columbus Day is missing!" she wailed.

Encyclopedia stood firm. After all, Candida was so absentminded that she could lose her sense of direction in an elevator. For her, losing Christopher Columbus Day was really no worse than losing any other Monday.

"When did Christopher Columbus Day disappear?" the detective inquired. "Last year?"

"This morning—oh, you don't understand," Candida protested. "Christopher Columbus Day is a goose. You've got to find him!"

"I'm on my way," Encyclopedia said.

Candida lived at a plant nursery. She hurried out of the house as Encyclopedia alighted from the Number 9 bus.

"Thank goodness you're here," she said. "Christopher Columbus Day is the best watchgoose we have."

She explained. For several years her father had been

troubled by people stealing supplies from the nursery—
bales of peat moss, topsoil, even shrubs.

"At first Dad tried watchdogs," she said. "They had
to be chained, and so they were good only for the length
of the chain. Also, Dad was afraid they might hurt someone."

She waved toward a group of five geese.

"Those geese were the answer," she said. "They can't
fly. They just roam about the place, winter and summer.
All they want is a kiddie pool to splash around in and
a little corn. They do the job."

"If honking geese could save ancient Rome from the
Gauls sneaking in at night, they ought to protect a nursery," Encyclopedia agreed.

"Their beaks are like vises," Candida said. "I've seen
them drive off stray dogs that got into the henhouse."
She turned. "C'mon, I'll show you around."

The tour took fifteen minutes. Encyclopedia found
not a single clue to the missing goose. He did notice,
however, that the back of the nursery bordered on Den-
isen Park, the state camping grounds.

Monday—the day after tomorrow—was the real
Christopher Columbus Day. Families in station wagons
and mobile homes were arriving at the park for the long
holiday weekend.

"Let's look in the park," Encyclopedia suggested.
"Christopher Columbus Day may have gone exploring."

As they headed for the park, the detective asked if
Christopher Columbus Day knew his own name.

"Nope, geese are free spirits," Candida replied. "Besides, although we named the watchgeese after holidays, we call them all Flatfoot. It saves time."

Encyclopedia was both disappointed and relieved by the news. He wondered if he really could have walked through the park calling, "Here, Christopher Columbus Day!" Especially this weekend.

The two children split up, agreeing to meet by the entrance booth in three hours. Candida took the western half of the park to search, Encyclopedia the eastern.

For nearly two hours the detective asked campers if they had seen a runaway goose. No one had, though they were all interested and tried to be helpful. The only exception was a tall, muscular woman. She wore a dark brown shirt, cutoff jeans, and hiking shoes, and she carried a large red knapsack.

"A goose? Are you kidding me, sonny?" she grumbled, and never broke stride.

A few minutes later, Encyclopedia found three feathers by a bright new mobile home. He was examining them when a white-haired man came up to him.

"I'm chasing a goose," Encyclopedia explained. He held out the feathers.

The man examined them. "These are chicken feathers," he said. "I know. I used to have a farm in Iowa before I retired last year. Raised turkeys and Rhode Island Reds on the side."

Encyclopedia thanked the man and moved on. It was nearly noon.

Most of the campers whom he questioned during the next half-hour were eating lunch or preparing to eat. One woman remembered seeing several boys chasing a rooster earlier that morning. But no one had seen a goose.

Encyclopedia was getting hungry himself when he spied two men eating by a fire. As he approached, one of the men called out, "What's wrong, young fella? Hungry? Have some chicken. There's plenty."

The second man held a spit with several parts—wings, neck, breast, and thighs—stuck on it. He flicked his knife and sliced off some meat from the breast.

"Nothing like hot-off-the-fire chicken," he said with a chuckle. The knife, with a slice of dark meat dangling from the tip, he shoved at Encyclopedia.

"Much obliged," Encyclopedia mumbled, plucking the meat free. "Have you seen a goose around here?"

"No," the first man said. "Hey, wait . . . we passed a bunch of them on the way to the park. At a plant nursery. Some woman with a red knapsack was feeding them."

"I should have guessed!" Encyclopedia said, and hurried off.

He jogged the remainder of his search area without success. The woman with the red knapsack had vanished. Disappointed, he made his way back to the entrance to meet Candida.

She was waiting for him. "Any luck?"

"I have a lead," Encyclopedia said. "Did you see a big woman with a red knapsack?"

"And a dark brown shirt?" Candida asked. "Sure. She nearly walked over me. Was she in a rush!"

"She's a suspect . . ." His voice trailed off. Then he smacked his thigh and said, "How slow of me!"

329

ENCYCLOPEDIA BROWN TAKES THE CAKE!

"Oh, dear," Candida said. "For a moment I thought you knew where Christopher Columbus Day is."

"I do," replied the detective. "But I needed your help."

WHAT DID ENCYCLOPEDIA MEAN?

(Turn to page **390** for the solution to The Case of the Missing Watchgoose.)

CHAPTER 10

AN ITALIAN DINNER

CANDIDA was crushed. Her pet watchgoose was gone, never to honk again.

Encyclopedia and Sally did their best to cheer her up. They told jokes and tried to get her to play games. Encyclopedia nearly suggested Duck Duck Goose, but caught himself.

After an hour, Candida was still weepy, still droopy. Nothing interested her or made her smile.

Encyclopedia was getting hungry. Remembering the watchgoose's fate, however, he said nothing.

Suddenly Candida dried her eyes. "I just realized that I haven't eaten all day, and I'm starving," she announced. "Let's go have a snack."

As they sat at the kitchen table, Encyclopedia mentioned that he and Sally had discovered that they loved to cook.

Candida brightened. "We ought to have an Italian dinner for Columbus Day," she said.

"Bravo!" cried Sally. "Let's have the dinner at my house."

"No, here," insisted Candida. "We could have it to celebrate Columbus Day, the holiday, and in memory of Christopher Columbus Day, my poor departed goose. My mother will help us make her world-famous spaghetti sauce. We'll have marvelous, fantastic, earthshaking Italian food."

That settled the matter nicely. Encyclopedia, Sally, and Candida each invited a friend to honor both Christopher Columbus Days. They cooked and ate an Italian dinner at Candida's house.

Here is their menu:

Spaghetti
Italian Cheese Salad
Garlic Bread

Lemon-Orange Italian Ice

SPAGHETTI

2 tablespoons butter

2 tablespoons salad oil (use olive oil, if you have any)

2 tablespoons finely chopped onion (or 1 tablespoon instant onion)

1 large can (about 28 ounces) crushed, chopped, or ground tomato

1 6-ounce can tomato paste

¼ cup water

2 teaspoons oregano

½ teaspoon salt

¼ teaspoon black pepper

¼ teaspoon sugar

1 1-pound box spaghetti

You will need:

large saucepan

large pot

colander

1. Melt the butter with the oil over low heat in a large saucepan. The pan should be large enough to hold all ingredients. Add the onion and cook, stirring constantly, for 3 minutes.

2. Add all the other ingredients except the spaghetti. Cook, uncovered, over very low heat for 20 minutes, stirring now and then. You can make the sauce ahead and reheat it at mealtime.

3. About 20 minutes before you want to eat, start heating a big pot of water. Cook the spaghetti according to the directions on the box. You'd better have a grown-up help you with cooking and draining it. After the spaghetti is drained, combine it with the sauce and serve.

Makes 6 big helpings. Some people like to have grated parmesan cheese on the table to sprinkle on their spaghetti.

ITALIAN CHEESE SALAD

    1 head lettuce
    1 medium tomato
    2 scallions
    ¼ pound Gorgonzola or blue cheese
    3 tablespoons salad oil
    1 tablespoon vinegar
    ¼ teaspoon salt

You will need:
    salad spinner or paper towels
    salad bowl
    small mixing bowl

1. Rinse the lettuce leaves in water. Dry them with paper towels or in a salad spinner.

2. Break the lettuce into very small pieces. Cut the tomato into small pieces. Chop the scallions by cutting a little piece off each end, removing and throwing away any dead leaves, then thinly slicing the stems crosswise. Put all these vegetables into a salad bowl.

3. Grate or crumble the cheese right on top of the ingredients in the bowl. Cover the bowl with foil or plastic wrap, then place in the refrigerator.

4. At serving time, combine the oil, vinegar, and salt. Pour over the top of the salad. Mix everything together.

Serves 6. If you don't like Gorgonzola or blue cheese, you can leave it out and substitute a can of chick peas or kidney beans, drained. It will be a different Italian salad, and just as good.

GARLIC BREAD

1 large clove garlic (or ¼ teaspoon garlic powder)
2 tablespoons soft (room temperature) butter or margarine
2 tablespoons salad oil
1 large loaf Italian or French bread

You will need:
garlic press (optional)
saucepan
bowl

1. If you're using a clove of garlic, put the garlic through a garlic press. Discard the peel. Combine the pulp, or garlic powder, with the butter and oil. Mix thoroughly. Let it sit for at least half an hour.

2. Cut the loaf of bread in half lengthwise. Spread the garlic mixture over the cut sides of the bread. Put the pieces, cut side up, on a baking sheet.

3. Preheat broiler. Shortly before you're ready to serve, broil the bread about 3 inches from the heat for 2 or 3 minutes—just until the garlic mixture is bubbling and turning brown. Watch closely, because it burns quickly.

4. After you remove the baking pan from the oven (remember to use oven mitts or thick potholders), put the two halves of the bread back together, so it looks like a loaf again. Cut down through it, crosswise, every 1½ inches to make single serving-sized pieces.

If you really love garlic, you can use 2 cloves instead of 1. That's the way Josh Whipplewhite likes his garlic bread.

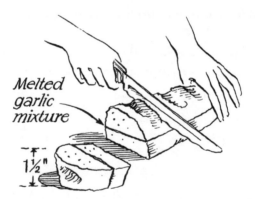

Melted
garlic
mixture

1½"

LEMON-ORANGE ITALIAN ICE

4 cups water
2 cups sugar
2 cups orange juice
Juice of 2 lemons

You will need:
medium-sized saucepan
10″ x 10″ baking pan

1. Combine the water and sugar in a medium-sized saucepan. Bring to a boil, stirring often, then boil over medium heat for 5 minutes.

2. Remove from heat until cool, then stir in the orange and lemon juices. Pour into a small (about 10″ x 10″) baking pan. Cover with foil or plastic wrap. Put in the freezer.

3. Let the mixture freeze undisturbed for half an hour, then stir it every half-hour for 1½ or 2 hours, until the ice is evenly frozen. Don't forget to do this, or you will have ice hard enough for the world's smallest skating rink instead of a good thing to eat.

CHAPTER 11

THE CASE OF
THE SECRET RECIPE

BEAUFORD Twitty was eleven and crazy about potatoes. He was the only person in the United States who ran a potato museum. Admission was by invitation only.

"You're invited to the museum tomorrow at noon," he told Sally and Encyclopedia before the regular Friday afternoon touch football game. "I'm holding a potato tasting hour to introduce Tubers a la Twitty!"

"What's that?" Sally asked politely.

"Tubers a la Twitty is a secret recipe for preparing the world's newest potato," Beauford answered. "I can't tell you more now."

"How about one tiny clue?" Encyclopedia requested.

"Not about the recipe," Beauford said. "I don't want you to form an opinion before you taste it. But I can tell you about the potatoes that I'll use. They're superspuds."

He explained. His Grandfather Twitty, who had a farm in New York, had been trying for years to breed a better potato. He had finally succeeded.

"Those potatoes are the best," Beauford said. "Grandpa

sent me a bagful to test on the all-important kids' market. So I'm trying them out on you and some of my other friends. Tomorrow is D-Day."

"I'm sure Tubers a la Twitty will be delicious," Sally said breathlessly.

"It will be sensational!" Beauford proclaimed. "It will make the name of Twitty famous in the field. Look at Bismarck, Melba, Napoleon, Tetrazzini, Caruso, and Reuben. They gained undying fame. Why? Because recipes were named after them!"

Encyclopedia nodded knowingly. It was the best he could do when Beauford got carried away by his favorite subject, potatoes.

Beauford started for the door and stopped.

"I almost forgot," he said. "I have another surprise. My grandpa sent me a big potato with the autographs of all the Yankee pitchers. I'll display it at the tasting tomorrow."

With that he departed, walking lightly, as if he were stepping on potato chips.

A little before noon on Saturday, the detectives presented themselves at Beauford's front door. Already there were the other guests: Flo Landis, Darlene Cutler, Sean McCoy, and Farnsworth Grant.

At exactly twelve o'clock, Beauford opened the door.

"Come in and look around," he said. "I'll need another few minutes with Tubers a la Twitty."

The potato museum was in the basement. Strewn all about were potato bags, mashers, sacks, peelers, and even an old plow. There were also jars of Colorado beetles — the potato farmer's number-one enemy — and examples of some of the world's thousands of potato varieties.

"I've cleaned up the kitchen," Beauford called down. "We'll eat as soon as I set the table."

"Let us help you," Sally shouted.

The guests climbed the stairs and went into the kitchen. It was spotless. Everything had been put away.

"My folks let me use the kitchen provided it was clean when they returned from Glenn City this afternoon," Beauford said.

The guests did not stand around admiring the cleanliness. Each one found something to do. Darlene got the silverware. Sean and Farnsworth found glasses and filled them with water. Flo got out a bottle of ketchup. Sally fetched the paper napkins.

"You can take these," Beauford said to Encyclopedia, handing him a pair of candlesticks. "They'll add the proper touch of class."

When the table was set, Beauford put an old record on the phonograph. The scratchy sounds of Louis Armstrong tooting "Potato Head Blues" filled the dining room.

In the center of the table was a large bowl sealed across the top with aluminum foil. "Behold!" exclaimed Beauford. He whipped off the aluminum foil with a sweep of his arm. In the bowl were French fries.

Beauford grinned. "What did you expect, potato pancakes Rhineland style? Or *Pommes de Terre Farcies*? You shouldn't ruin magnificent potatoes with fancy cooking!"

The French fries were passed around. Farnsworth reached for the ketchup. Beauford howled in pain.

"You've got to taste them pure!" he cried.

The French fries were gobbled pure. They were the best French fries the guests had ever tasted.

"Think what a boon to the fast food industry my grandfather's potatoes will be," Beauford said, beaming with pleasure.

"What about the potato with the autographs of the New York Yankee pitchers?" asked Farnsworth, who at heart was a Chicago Cubs fan.

"Coming up," Beauford said. He hurried to the basement and brought back a small sack. Carefully he reached inside and pulled out a potato.

It was naked. There wasn't a single autograph on it.

Beauford sank weakly into his chair. "I've been robbed," he gasped.

"Who knew about the potato with the autographs?" Sally asked.

"Only you six," Beauford replied dully.

"Encyclopedia," Sally whispered. "Say something! Ask a question!"

Encyclopedia wondered if Sally thought he was a detective or a magician. Still, he did have one important clue. . . .

"Was the back door unlocked today?" he inquired.

"Y-yes," Beauford replied. "The doors are never locked during the day if someone is at home."

"Then excuse me," Encyclopedia said. He went outside and walked around the house. He stopped to peer into the kitchen.

When he returned to the dining room, he spoke to one of the guests.

"Would you kindly return the potato you stole?" he said softly.

WHO WAS THE THIEF?

(Turn to page 391 for the solution to
The Case of the Secret Recipe.)

CHAPTER 12

DINNER AT
THE TWITTYS'

ENCYCLOPEDIA had set right the world of Beauford Twitty. Flo had returned the potato with the autographs of the Yankee pitchers. The potato museum was back to normal — still a mess, but complete.

"I'm going to clean up the museum," Beauford vowed as he and Encyclopedia sat in the Brown Detective Agency on Sunday. "I have a great idea. The exhibits will be color-graded."

"How's that?" questioned Encyclopedia.

"My potatoes will be displayed by color, from skins of brownish white to deep purple," Beauford explained.

"Spruce up the spuds," Encyclopedia said, "and your museum could double as a modern art gallery. Imagine, art that can be eaten! You'll be the toast of two continents."

Beauford shrugged. "I'm not into modern art," he said. "I'm into potatoes. Anyone can understand potatoes. They don't need excuses."

Beauford got to his feet. "I stopped by to thank you for your detective work," he said. "And to invite you over for dinner tomorrow. I'm going to cook it all myself, without one potato recipe. Can you come?"

Encyclopedia accepted eagerly and added, "I'd like to help with the cooking."

"I can use help," confessed Beauford. "Come at five o'clock, then."

Encyclopedia arrived promptly at five. Here is the dinner he and Beauford cooked:

Cream of Chicken Soup

Meat Loaf
Corn Pudding
Baked Tomatoes
Lemon-Buttered Green Beans

Idaville Apple Pie

345

CREAM OF CHICKEN SOUP

Parsley, three or four sprigs, torn apart
2 10¾-ounce cans condensed chicken broth
1½ cups water
1 teaspoon salt
1 cup (1 8-ounce carton) medium or heavy cream
A dash of cinnamon

You will need:
scissors
saucepans (2)

1. Cut the parsley up with a pair of scissors. Don't use the heavy stems, just the leaves and the tiny stems to which they're attached.

2. Place the chicken broth, water, and salt in one saucepan, the cream in another. Warm both over low heat. Be sure not to let the cream boil. Remove from heat.

3. Pour the cream slowly into the broth. Sprinkle on the cinnamon. Stir. Sprinkle each serving with a little of the parsley.

Makes 6 small servings or 3 or 4 bigger ones.

MRS. TWITTY'S MEAT LOAF

3 slices bread, crumbled
1 cup milk
1 egg

¼ cup minced onion (or 2 tablespoons instant onion mixed with 2 tablespoons water)

1 teaspoon salt

1 tablespoon Worcestershire sauce

1½ pounds ground beef

6 slices bacon (optional)

You will need:
mixing bowl
wooden spoon (optional)
loaf pan

1. Preheat oven to 350°F.

2. Mix the bread, milk, egg, onion, salt, and Worcestershire sauce together in a bowl, then mix in the ground beef. Use a wooden spoon or your hands.

3. If you're using the bacon, put 3 slices of it in a loaf pan, lengthwise. Put the meat mixture in next, then top with the other 3 bacon slices. If you're not using the bacon, just put the meat loaf mixture in a loaf pan.

4. Bake for 1 hour and 15 minutes. Let cool for 15 minutes after you remove it from the oven so it will be easier to slice.

Serves 6. If there is any meat loaf left, you can have cold meat loaf for dinner another night or make sandwiches with the leftovers.

CORN PUDDING

---

1 tablespoon soft butter or margarine
2 eggs
2 1-pound cans cream-style corn
1 teaspoon salt

You will need:
baking dish
2 mixing bowls

1. Preheat oven to 350°F. (It will already be on if you're cooking this whole meal.) Grease a baking dish with the butter or margarine.

2. Beat the eggs a little with a fork in a small bowl or in a blender. Put the corn into a bowl and mix in the salt and the eggs. Put into the baking dish. Bake for 45 minutes. (If you're serving the whole dinner, put the corn pudding in the oven after the meat loaf has cooked for 45 minutes.)

Serves 6. To make half this recipe, use 1 can of corn, 1 egg, and ½ teaspoon of salt, but still use 1 tablespoon of butter to grease the baking dish.

BAKED TOMATOES

---

3 medium-sized tomatoes
½ teaspoon salt
1 tablespoon salad oil (plus a little more to oil the baking pan)
4 tablespoons grated cheese

½ teaspoon dried oregano or basil

3 tablespoons soft bread crumbs (crumble 1 slice of bread with your hands)

3 tablespoons butter or margarine, cut into 6 slices

You will need:
small baking pan

1. Preheat oven to 350°F. (It will already be heated if you're cooking this whole meal.) Oil a small pan.

2. Wash the tomatoes in cold water. Cut them in half across the middle. Using your fingers or a small spoon, scoop out and throw away the seeds and the liquid around them. Sprinkle the tomatoes with salt, then turn them upside down on paper towels to drain for ten minutes. Now put them, cut side up, in the oiled baking pan.

3. Combine the salad oil, cheese, and oregano or basil. Stuff this mixture into the holes in the tomatoes where the seeds used to be. Sprinkle some of the bread crumbs on each tomato half, then press a slice of butter on top.

4. Shortly before you want to eat (after the meat loaf has cooked for 1 hour and 10 minutes), bake the tomatoes for 20 minutes.

Serves 3 or 6, depending on whether each person eats one tomato half or two.

LEMON-BUTTERED GREEN BEANS

2 packages frozen whole green beans (or 2
  pounds fresh green beans)
4 tablespoons butter
½ teaspoon salt (plus more if you use fresh beans)
1 tablespoon lemon juice (the juice of ½ lemon)

You will need:
  large pot
  colander
  large frying pan

1. Cook the frozen beans about 2 minutes less than the package instructions say. (If you use fresh beans, wash them, break off the ends, and cook them for 10 minutes in a big pot of boiling salted water — about 1 tablespoon of salt to 2 quarts of water.) Drain them in a colander.

2. Melt the butter in a big frying pan. Add the ½ teaspoon salt, then the beans. Cook over medium heat for 3 minutes, stirring carefully so you don't break the beans. Stir in the lemon juice.

Serves 6. To serve 3, use 1 package frozen green beans, 2 tablespoons butter, ¼ teaspoon salt, and 1½ teaspoons lemon juice.

IDAVILLE APPLE PIE

2 frozen pie crust shells
6 medium-sized apples (Red or Golden
  Delicious or Cortland are best)

⅓ cup granulated sugar
⅓ cup light brown sugar
¼ teaspoon cinnamon
⅛ teaspoon nutmeg
1 tablespoon cornstarch
2 tablespoons butter

You will need:
mixing bowl

1. Preheat oven to 450°F.

2. Thaw pie crust shells. Leave one in pie pan. Put the other on a flat surface for now. (It will be your top crust.)

3. Peel and core apples. Slice thin. Put slices into a bowl.

4. Combine both kinds of sugar with the cinnamon, nutmeg, and cornstarch. Sprinkle over the apple slices. Mix together gently. Put into crust in pie pan. Put little bits of the butter here and there all over.

5. Put the top crust on. Pinch its edge together with the edge of the bottom crust, then press flat against the top edge of the pie pan with the tines of a fork. Cut two or three slits in the top.

6. Bake at 450°F for 10 minutes, then reduce temperature setting to 350°F and bake for 35 minutes more.

Serves 4 to 8.

CHAPTER 13

THE CASE
OF
THE CHINESE
RESTAURANT

OLIVER Wilkie was fourteen and loved Chinese food. He was known by some as the Cantonese Kid. Others called him the Subgum Submarine because of the way he dived into any dish flavored with Oriental vegetables.

Whenever he had spare cash, he spent it at the Chinese restaurant near the junior high school. Usually he bought a takeout order of egg rolls or barbecued spareribs, which he ate by the duck pond behind the restaurant.

When he rang Encyclopedia Brown's doorbell, he looked as though a toothache would make him happy.

"I need your help," he said to the detective. "I could go to prison."

"Come in," said Encyclopedia. "You'd better sit down. What's the crime?"

"I'm supposed to have stolen a hundred and eight dollars," he said. "I didn't. The money disappeared from my schoolbag while I was in the Chinese restaurant Monday. The next day the restaurant went out of business."

"Oh," Sally said sympathetically.

"Oh, oh," corrected Oliver. "First I'm accused of stealing. Then the restaurant folds. I've been hit with a one-two punch to the head and stomach."

"Who says you stole the money?" Encyclopedia asked.

"Mitch Landon and Kate Walters," Oliver answered. "Since I beat Kate in the election for treasurer of the Service Club, she's had it in for me. She and Mitch are very close. They play mixed doubles on the tennis team."

"What do they say about the missing money?" Sally asked.

"I haven't time to tell you now," Oliver replied. "I'm already late for my piano lesson. But Monday at three o'clock there'll be a hearing in the principal's office. Can you be there?"

"Yes, and don't worry," Encyclopedia said. "Everything will turn out all right."

He spoke encouragingly, but he didn't feel encouraged at all. The case was like the start of an ice cream sundae. He didn't know what was going on.

Nonetheless, on Monday he and Sally joined Oliver, Kate, and Mitch in the office of Mr. Gerard, the junior high school principal.

As the detectives found seats, Mr. Gerard gazed at them questioningly. Oliver explained why they were there. Mr. Gerard nodded his permission for them to remain.

"This is not a trial," Mr. Gerard began. He was a soft-spoken man, popular with students and teachers alike. "We are here in an attempt to reach the truth about the missing money."

In a steady, quiet voice he reviewed for Encyclopedia and Sally the background of the case.

Each year, dues from all the school's clubs were put in the bank by the treasurer of one of the clubs. This

year the deposits were made by the treasurer of the Service Club—Oliver.

Before Oliver had set out for the bank, Mitch had handed him an envelope with money from the Lettermen's Club, of which Mitch was treasurer. Mr. Bertram, the club's advisor, had signed his name across the sealed flap of the envelope.

Oliver had put the envelope into his schoolbag along with those from the other clubs. On his way to the bank, he had stopped at the Chinese restaurant.

Because it was raining, he had decided not to go to the duck pond with a takeout order. Instead, he sat down at a table in the rear room.

A minute later, Mitch and Kate came in and took a table near his. It was after the lunch hour, and the three children were alone in the room.

Mr. Gerard looked at Oliver and then at Kate and Mitch. "Now," he said, "we come to the point of disagreement. I want your side first, Oliver."

Oliver cleared his throat nervously.

"After I'd sat down at the table, I noticed my hands were dirty," he said. "So I asked Mitch and Kate to watch my schoolbag while I washed. It was the only time I let my schoolbag out of my sight till I reached the bank and found the Lettermen's Club envelope missing."

Mr. Gerard thanked Oliver politely. Then the principal invited Kate and Mitch to tell their side.

"Oliver never spoke a word to us in the restaurant," Kate insisted. "When we got there, he was holding an envelope to the light. He slit it open with a table knife and peered inside. At that point he noticed us. He slipped the money from the envelope into his pocket, grabbed his schoolbag, and raced outside."

Mr. Gerard brought his fingers together and pressed the tips against his chin thoughtfully. "Does anyone have anything to add?" he inquired.

Encyclopedia raised his hand. "Sir," he said. "May I ask a question?"

"If you think it will help," Mr. Gerard answered.

"I'd like to ask Kate and Mitch if Oliver had placed his food order?"

"No," Mitch said. "Just as we sat down, a waiter brought a menu to his table. Find the waiter. He must have seen Oliver with the money in his hand."

"You can't find the waiter, and you know it!" Oliver cried. "The restaurant went out of business!"

"We do have one piece of evidence," Mr. Gerard said. He held up an envelope, slit open along the flap. "This is the envelope that held the Lettermen's Club money, according to Mr. Bertram, the club's advisor. He recognized it by his signature on the back."

Kate said, "When Oliver jumped up and ran out of the restaurant, he left the empty envelope behind."

Sally leaned toward Encyclopedia. "It looks very bad for Oliver," she whispered.

"Wrong," replied the detective. "It looks very bad for Kate and Mitch."

WHY?

(Turn to page 392 for the solution to
The Case of the Chinese Restaurant.)

CHAPTER 14

A CHINESE BANQUET

AMERICA's Sherlock Holmes in sneakers had done it again—cracked a seemingly uncrackable mystery.

Oliver was grateful but glum. "I'm giving up Chinese food," he said.

"Whatever for?" demanded Sally. "It's delicious."

"And dangerous," asserted Oliver. "Look where it got me. Into big trouble. I ask you seriously, who ever got ahead in life by eating Chinese food?"

"I Yin, for one," said Encyclopedia.

"Who's he?" Oliver asked suspiciously.

"He was a cook to King T'ang of Shang, founder of the T'ang dynasty in China," Encyclopedia said. "Eventually he became the king's prime minister. Some scholars say it was I Yin's skill as a cook that won him the job."

"From cook to prime minister?" Oliver gasped. "Really?"

"It's history," Encyclopedia said.

"You've made me feel better already," Oliver declared. "In fact, I'm getting hungry for some egg rolls and an order of sweet and sour meatballs."

"Oh, Oliver," Sally protested. "Have you forgotten? The Chinese restaurant went out of business."

"I did forget." Oliver moaned and bowed his head.

"Things aren't so bad," Encyclopedia said. "My mother cooks a Chinese dish now and then. We could take her recipes and put them all together. It would be a banquet!"

Oliver perked up. "Could I invite my little brother?"

"Bring him along," Encyclopedia invited. "We'll make enough for six."

And they did. Here's what they had:

Egg Drop Soup

Chinese Riblets
Egg Rolls with Chinese Sauces:
Duck Sauce
Hot Chinese Mustard Sauce
Sweet and Sour Meatballs
Chinese-style Rice

Oriental Fruit Cocktail

EGG DROP SOUP

6 cups chicken broth (you can make this with 3 10-ounce cans of concentrated chicken broth and 2¼ measuring cups of water)

2 eggs

1 big scallion (or 2 small ones)

2 tablespoons cornstarch combined with ¼ cup water

You will need:
    medium-sized saucepan
    small bowl or blender

1. Put the broth in a medium-sized saucepan. Start heating it over fairly low heat. Beat the eggs lightly in a small bowl or a blender. Trim a little off each end of the scallion. Slice it very thinly.

2. When the broth comes to a boil, stir in cornstarch mixture, then remove the pan from the heat. Pour in the beaten eggs with one hand while you stir the broth with the other, then stir in the slices of scallion.

Serve right away to 6 people.

CHINESE RIBLETS

½ cup soy sauce

½ cup honey

½ cup catsup

1 clove of garlic, crushed in a garlic press (can be left out if you don't like garlic)

½ teaspoon ground ginger

¼ cup water

3 pounds small pork spareribs or lean breast of lamb, cut in small sections of two or three ribs each

You will need:

mixing bowl or pan

baking pan

1. Combine the soy sauce, honey, catsup, garlic (if you're using it), ginger, and water. Put in a bowl or pan with the ribs. Make sure the ribs are well coated with the sauce.

2. Cover the pan with foil or plastic wrap, then place it in the refrigerator for about 3 hours. (If you don't have 3 hours to spare, you can skip this step, but it helps the flavor of the sauce to get all through the meat.)

3. Preheat oven to 325°F. Lift ribs out of sauce. Put them on a rack in a baking pan. Bake for 1½ hours, spooning some of the sauce over the ribs three or four times, until all of the marinade is used.

Serves 6.

EGG ROLLS WITH CHINESE SAUCES

Egg rolls are very hard to make from scratch, so buy the frozen ones. Follow the instructions on the package and allow one or two egg rolls for each person at the banquet. Serve the egg rolls with hot Chinese mustard and duck sauce (sometimes called plum sauce). You can buy these in most supermarkets, but it's more fun to make them.

DUCK SAUCE

½ cup plum jam or preserves
2 tablespoons apple sauce
5 tablespoons cider vinegar
1 teaspoon sugar

You will need:
small bowl

1. Stir everything together in a small bowl.

2. That's all!

HOT CHINESE MUSTARD SAUCE

2 tablespoons dry mustard
2 tablespoons water

You will need: small bowl

1. About half an hour before you want to eat, stir the mustard and water together. Place on a small plate or saucer.

2. Don't use more than a tiny bit of this—it's HOT.

SWEET AND SOUR MEATBALLS

For the meatballs:
  - 1½ pounds ground beef
  - 2 tablespoons finely chopped onion (or 1 tablespoon instant onion plus 1 tablespoon water)
  - ½ teaspoon salt
  - 2 tablespoons salad oil

For the sauce:
  - 3 carrots
  - 2 green peppers
  - 2 tomatoes
  - 1 20-ounce can pineapple chunks, drained (save the juice)
  - 2 tablespoons brown sugar
  - ¼ cup vinegar
  - 1 teaspoon salt
  - 2 tablespoons cornstarch
  - ½ cup water

You will need:
  mixing bowl
  frying pan
  vegetable peeler
  medium-sized saucepan with lid

1. *Make the meatballs.* Mix the beef with the onion and ½ teaspoon salt in a bowl. Make it into balls a little smaller than walnuts. Cook them in the oil in a frying pan over moderate heat until they're brown—keep turning them over with a spoon as they cook. Remove pan from heat.

2. *Prepare the vegetables. Carrots:* Peel (away from you) with a vegetable peeler. Slice as thin as you can. *Green Peppers:* Cut in two from top to bottom. Throw away the seeds and stem end; cut the rest into small slivers. *Tomatoes:* Cut in half; throw away the seeds and stem ends; cut into medium-sized chunks.

3. *Make the sauce.* Measure the juice you drained off the pineapple. Add enough water to make 1 cup. Put in a medium-sized saucepan with the brown sugar, vinegar, and 1 teaspoon salt. Bring to a boil; turn down heat. Add the carrots. Cover pan; cook for 10 minutes over low heat. Add the meatballs, green peppers, tomatoes, and pineapple. Then mix the 2 tablespoons of cornstarch with the ½ cup of water and stir this into the mixture in the pan. Keep on stirring, still over low heat, until the mixture comes to a boil and changes from cloudy-looking to clear. Remove pan from heat. Serve now, or reheat and serve later.

Serves 6.

CHINESE-STYLE RICE

You will need:
    strainer
    medium-sized saucepan with lid

1. Take 1 cup of long grain rice. Put it in a strainer. Hold the strainer under cold running water for 3 minutes, moving it around so all the rice is thoroughly washed.

2. Put the rice in a medium-sized saucepan that has a tight-fitting lid. Add enough cold water to cover the rice by 1 inch. Don't put the cover on the pan yet.

3. Bring the water to a boil over high heat, then let it boil hard for 4 minutes, or until most of the water has boiled off.

4. Turn heat very low. Put the cover on the pot. Cook for 15 minutes more. Stir with a fork before serving. Makes 3 cups rice, which will make a small serving each for 6 people. If you want more, just use more rice. The recipe always works, as long as you add water to cover the raw rice by 1 inch.

ORIENTAL FRUIT COCKTAIL

    6 apples
    1 8-ounce can water chestnuts
    1 6-ounce can frozen orange juice, thawed
        but not diluted
    1 1-pound can crushed pineapple
    ¼ cup ginger marmalade

You will need:
vegetable peeler
mixing bowl

1. Peel and core the apples. Chop them into small pieces. Drain the liquid off the water chestnuts. Cut or slice them into fairly small pieces.

2. Put the chopped apples and water chestnuts into a bowl. Add the orange juice, pineapple, and ginger marmalade. Stir well. Chill until you're ready to serve.

Serves 6. If you can't find ginger marmalade in a grocery store, you can use ½ teaspoon ground ginger instead, plus ¼ cup orange marmalade. You can find water chestnuts in the Chinese section of most supermarkets.

This is a small Chinese banquet.

A large one might contain
chicken cooked three different ways,
lobster cooked two ways,
shrimp,
roast suckling pig,
a sweet and sour dish,
duckling,
beef cooked two different ways,
two or three fish dishes,
and three soups,
one of which is sweet
and is considered dessert.

CHAPTER 15

SNACKS
AND
LUNCHES

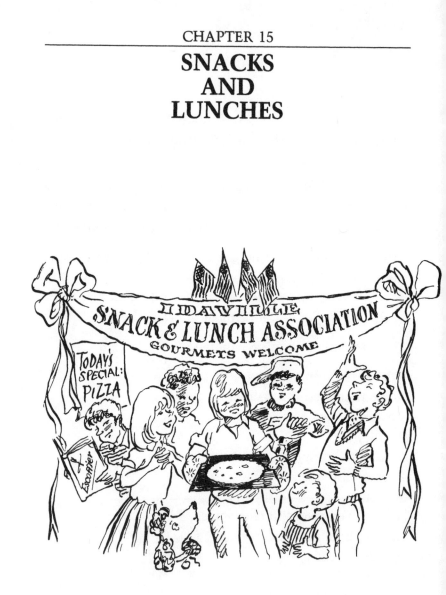

ENCYCLOPEDIA and his friends don't just cook dinners.
Lots of times they fix snacks and lunches. Here are some
of the things they make.

PIZZA

___

4 loaves pocket bread (also called pita bread,
   Syrian bread, etc.)
1 8-ounce can or small jar pizza sauce (or use
   some of the spaghetti sauce from page 61)
8 tablespoons shredded mozzarella cheese
4 tablespoons grated Parmesan cheese
2 teaspoons oregano (or basil or Italian
   seasoning)

You will need:
baking sheet

1. Preheat oven to 350°F.

2. Put the whole loaves of pocket bread, wrong side up, on a baking sheet. Spread about ¼ cup pizza sauce on each one. Cover all the bread except for a narrow border around the rim. Sprinkle part of the mozzarella cheese on each piece of bread, then do the same with the Parmesan cheese and oregano.

3. Bake for just 4 or 5 minutes, or until the mozzarella cheese is melted.

Makes 4 small individual pizzas. If you don't have mozzarella cheese, you can use cheddar instead. Also, if you can't find pocket bread in a store, you can use small loaves of French bread. (Cut them in two lengthwise first.) Split English muffins make good pizzas, too.

SLIPPERY JOES

---

1 teaspoon salad oil
1 pound chopped beef
¼ cup minced onion (or 2 tablespoons instant onion plus 2 tablespoons water)
1 cup catsup
4 hamburger rolls

You will need:
medium-sized frying pan or saucepan

1. Put the salad oil in a medium-sized frying pan or saucepan. Add the beef and onion. Cook and stir over medium heat until the color of all the meat changes from pink to light tan.

2. Stir in the catsup. Cook over very low heat, stirring often, for 5 minutes.

3. Split the hamburger rolls open. Spoon the Slippery Joe mixture onto the bottom halves, then cover with the top halves. Or, to make open-faced sandwiches, put the bun halves, cut side up, on plates, then spoon on the Slippery Joe mixture.

Makes 4.

HIDDEN VALLEY SANDWICHES

---

1 tablespoon butter or margarine
2 slices bread (whole wheat is good for this)
½ small apple, peeled, cored, and thinly sliced (eat the other half of the apple)

    1 tablespoon raisins
    2 slices cheddar cheese (use natural cheddar, if possible)

You will need:
    baking pan
    spatula or pancake turner

1. Preheat oven to 375°F.

2. Use the butter to grease a baking pan. Put the bread on this. On top of the bread, put a layer of apple slices, then the raisins, then the cheese.

3. Bake for 10 minutes or until the cheese is bubbly. Remove from the pan carefully with a wide spatula or pancake turner.

Serves 1 or 2. For plain open-faced grilled cheese sandwiches, leave out the raisins and apple. In this case, you may want to spread the top side of the bread with a little mustard before you put the cheese on it.

ALPINE SANDWICHES

    1 French roll or 2 slices bread (if you use bread, you'll also need 1 tablespoon butter or margarine)
    2 slices Swiss cheese
    2 very thin slices onion (optional)

You will need:
    baking sheet
    spatula or pancake turner

1. Preheat oven to 375°F.

2. Cut the French roll in half lengthwise. Put the pieces, cut side up, on a baking sheet. If you're using sliced bread instead, grease a baking sheet with 1 tablespoon of butter, then put the bread slices on that.

3. Cut the cheese into little pieces. Put them on the roll or bread. Top with the onion slices, if you're using them.

4. Bake for 10 minutes or until the cheese is bubbly. Remove from the pan carefully with a wide spatula or pancake turner.

Serves 1 or 2. Sometimes Encyclopedia likes to spread a spoonful or two of Italian salad dressing on the cut sides of the roll before he puts on the cheese and onion.

VOLCANO SANDWICHES

2 tablespoons butter
2 slices bread
2 slices pineapple
2 slices any kind of cheese
1 banana
1 tablespoon coconut

You will need:
baking pan
medium-sized frying pan
spatula or pancake turner

1. Preheat oven to 375°F. Use 1 tablespoon of the butter to grease a baking pan. Put the bread on this.

2. Put a slice of pineapple on top of each piece of bread, then a slice of cheese.

3. Peel the banana, cut it in half across the middle, then cut each piece in half lengthwise. Melt the other 1 tablespoon butter in a medium-sized frying pan over medium heat. Cook the banana pieces in this, turning them carefully with two spoons, until they just begin to brown. Now carefully, still using a spoon in each hand, lift the banana pieces out of the frying pan and arrange them on the sandwiches so they will look like lava coming down. Sprinkle on the coconut.

4. Bake for 10 minutes. (Take a look at the sandwiches after 7 minutes, though, because you don't want them to burn.) Remove from the pan very carefully with a wide spatula or pancake turner.

Makes 2 sandwiches.

SPECIAL COLD SANDWICHES

You make most of these just the way you do a peanut butter and jelly sandwich. (Spread the filling on two slices of bread, put the slices together with the filling in the middle, cut the sandwich in two if you want to—and away you go.)

1. Use cream cheese on raisin or nut bread. This sandwich doesn't need anything else, but you can add raisins if you want.

2. Mash cream cheese with a few slices of ripe banana. (Eat the rest of the banana.)

3. Use peanut butter with sliced banana.

4. Use lettuce leaves instead of bread. Spread their inside part with mayonnaise. Fill with slices of bologna, ham, or cheese.

5. Spread slices of bologna, ham, or salami with cream cheese or any cheese spread. Either put two pieces together or roll each piece up. In either case, have the filling in the middle.

6. Spread pickle relish on one piece of bread. Top with a slice of cold, leftover meat loaf, then another slice of bread. Or don't use bread at all—just two slices of cold meat loaf, with pickle relish in the middle.

7. Use thin slices of peeled cucumber between pieces of bread that have been spread on the inside with mayonnaise.

8. Make a pickle sandwich: Use bread and butter pickles between slices of buttered bread.

9. Use cottage cheese and peach jam (especially good on whole wheat toast).

10. Use liverwurst and lettuce between slices of rye bread that have been spread on the inside with mustard and mayonnaise.

TUBERS A LA TWITTY

(Oven-Baked French Fries)

1 large potato per person, scrubbed but not peeled
1 tablespoon salad oil per potato
1 tablespoon water per potato
Salt

You will need:
    large bowl
    cutting board
    baking tins
    spatula or 2 big spoons

1. Preheat oven to 375°F.

2. Combine the oil and water in a large bowl.

3. Cut a sliver off one side of each of the potatoes so they will stay flat on a cutting board, then cut them into ⅜" slices. Stack several of the slices together and cut down through them at ⅜" intervals. Put the pieces into the oil and water and toss around until they're well coated. Repeat until all the potatoes are cut and coated.

4. Spread the potatoes out on one or more baking tins so that they are one layer deep and not touching each other.

5. Bake for 40 minutes, turning the fries over once with a spatula or two big spoons after they've cooked 20 minutes. Sprinkle with salt to taste.

FRENCH FRENCH TOAST

To make the toast:
> 2 eggs
> ½ cup milk
> Butter for frying
> 8 to 10 1½-inch slices French (or Italian) bread

To serve it:
> Confectioners' sugar and jelly or jam
> *or* Butter or margarine and syrup

You will need:
> mixing bowl or blender
> griddle or frying pan
> pie pan

1. Beat the eggs and milk together in a bowl, just until they're blended. (If you have a blender, use it for this.) Pour into a pie pan.

2. Heat a griddle or frying pan over medium heat. Melt about a teaspoon of butter in it.

3. Dip both sides of the slices of bread into the egg and milk mixture. Fry on both sides until speckled brown. After each batch of bread is cooked, add more butter to the griddle or frying pan.

4. To serve, either sprinkle with confectioners' sugar and put a spoonful of jelly or jam on each slice, or serve with butter and syrup, just the way you would pancakes.

Serves 4 or 5. You can make regular French toast the same way by using slices of whatever bread you have on hand.

TANGERINOS OR TANGELINOS

4 tangerines or tangelos
⅓ cup honey
½ cup chopped nuts, or ½ cup coconut

You will need:
small mixing bowls (2)
baking pans or pie tins

1. Separate the tangerines or tangelos into sections. Pull off any loose white strings.

2. Put the honey and the nuts or coconut into separate small bowls.

3. One at a time, dip the sections in the honey, then into the nuts or coconut. (Use your fingers to do this.) Put the fruit sections on baking pans or pie tins that will fit in your freezer. Make sure the sections don't touch each other.

4. Freeze for at least 1 hour. Eat while they're still frozen. Recipe makes a lot — how much depends on how many sections there are in each tangerine or tangelo.

If you use tangerines, call these Tangerinos.
If you use tangelos, then they're Tangelinos.

BANANA SMASH

6 ripe bananas
1 tablespoon honey
1 tablespoon lemon juice (the juice of ½ lemon)

375

You will need:
  mixing bowl
  freezer container or small tin with lid

1. Put the bananas, honey, and lemon juice in a bowl. Mash it all together with a fork. (It doesn't have to be absolutely smooth, just well smashed.)

2. Put the mixture into a freezer container or small tin. Cover it and put it in the freezer for at least 4 hours (or for as long as 2 weeks). If the banana smash is very hard when you take it out of the freezer, let it sit at room temperature for about 45 minutes before serving. Good by itself or with cake or whipped cream/

Makes 4 big servings.

OATMEAL COOKIES

½ cup (1 stick) butter or margarine, at room temperature
½ cup light brown sugar (pack it down firmly while measuring)
½ cup white sugar
1 teaspoon vanilla
1 egg, unbeaten
⅔ cup unsifted flour
½ teaspoon baking soda
½ teaspoon salt
1 teaspoon cinnamon
1½ cups oatmeal (uncooked)

For all cookie recipes, you will need:
    baking tins (2 or 3)
    mixing bowls (2)
    spoon or electric mixer
    spatula or pancake turner

1. Preheat oven to 375°F. Lightly grease two or three baking tins (see below).

2. Combine the butter with both kinds of sugar and the vanilla and egg in a mixing bowl. Mix well with a spoon or electric mixer.

3. Mix the flour, baking soda, salt, and cinnamon together in a small bowl. Add this, bit by bit, to the butter mixture. Stir in the oatmeal.

4. Drop onto the baking tins by scooping up a slightly heaping spoonful of the cookie dough with a regular tea or coffee spoon, then pushing the dough off onto the tins with the back of the bowl of another spoon. Keep the cookies about 1½" apart, as they will spread. You can fit 20 to 24 cookies on a big tin. If your tins are small, you may have to use three of them or use the same one two or three times, regreasing it every time.

5. Bake, one tin at a time, on the top shelf of the oven for 8 to 12 minutes, or until the cookies begin to brown. Let them cool slightly on the tins, out of the oven, before lifting them off with a spatula. Makes about 40 cookies.

CHOCOLATE CHIP COOKIES

Follow the recipe for oatmeal cookies, but make these changes: Increase the flour to 1 cup; don't use the cinnamon; instead of using oatmeal, stir in 1 6-ounce package of semisweet real chocolate bits. (You can also add ½ cup chopped pecans or walnuts, if you like.)

COCONUT-OATMEAL COOKIES

Follow the recipe for oatmeal cookies, but add ⅓ cup coconut when you stir in the oatmeal.

RAISIN-OATMEAL COOKIES

Follow the recipe for oatmeal cookies, but add ¾ cup raisins when you stir in the oatmeal.

MONSTER COOKIES

Any of these cookies can be made in "monster" size. Use an ice cream scoop to measure and move the dough, then slightly flatten each mound with the back of a spoon. Bake only three cookies at a time.

ENCYCLOPEDIA BROWNIES

- ½ stick (2 ounces) plus 1 tablespoon butter or margarine
- 1 cup brown sugar, firmly packed in cup while measuring
- 1 egg

    ½ cup flour
    ⅛ teaspoon salt
    ½ teaspoon pure vanilla
    1 6-ounce package semisweet chocolate bits

You will need:
    8" x 8" baking pan
    large saucepan
    spatula or pancake turner

1. Preheat oven to 325°F. Use the 1 tablespoon of butter or margarine to grease an 8" x 8" baking pan.

2. Melt the rest of the butter or margarine over low heat in a saucepan large enough to hold all the ingredients. Remove from heat. Mix the brown sugar in well, then let cool for 10 minutes, or until lukewarm.

3. Stir the egg, then the flour, salt, and vanilla into the brown sugar mixture. Spread out evenly in the prepared pan. Sprinkle the chocolate evenly on top of the batter.

4. Bake for 25 to 35 minutes, or until the edges of the brownie mixture are pulling away from the pan and the top is shiny and somewhat wrinkled around the chocolate bits. (The mixture will still be very soft.) Let cool for 15 minutes, then cut into small squares, but don't remove from the pan until completely cool. Use a spatula to remove them.

These brownies are thin and chewy and seem almost like candy. If you'd rather have brownies with no chocolate at all in them you can substitute butterscotch or caramel bits for the chocolate ones.

SALLY'S DOUBLE-CHOCOLATE BROWNIES

½ pound (2 sticks) plus 1 tablespoon butter or margarine

4 ounces unsweetened baking chocolate

4 eggs

2 cups sugar

1 teaspoon pure vanilla

1 cup plus 2 tablespoons pre-sifted flour

1 6-ounce package semisweet real chocolate bits

½ cup chopped walnuts or pecans (optional)

You will need:

12" x 8" or 11" x 9" baking pan

double boiler

mixing bowl

electric mixer

spatula

1. Preheat oven to 350°F. Grease a 12" x 8" or 11" x 9" pan with the 1 tablespoon of butter or margarine. Put the 2 tablespoons of flour in the pan and tip it around until it covers the bottom of the pan. Shake any excess out into the kitchen sink.

2. Melt the rest of the butter or margarine and the unsweetened chocolate in a double boiler. Remove from heat; let cool for 10 minutes.

3. When the chocolate mixture is lukewarm, beat the eggs and sugar together in a bowl, perferably using an electric mixer, until they're thick and fluffy. With the

machine running slowly, add the chocolate mixture and the vanilla. Then, ¼ cup at a time, mix in the flour. Next, stir in the chocolate bits and the nuts (if you're using them) by hand.

4. Spread the batter evenly in the baking pan. Bake for 30 to 45 minutes, or until the top is shiny and the edges are pulling away from the pan. (The mixture will still be quite soft.) Cut the brownies into squares while they are still slightly warm, but don't remove from the pan until they are completely cool.

FROSTED CHOCOLATE

1 cup milk
¼ cup canned or bottled chocolate syrup
2 scoops vanilla ice cream

You will need:
blender or screw-top jar

Put all the ingredients into the container of a blender. Put the cover of the blender on tightly. Run the machine until everything is well mixed. (If you don't have a blender, put everything in a big screw-top jar with the top on tightly and shake, shake, shake it.)

Serves 1.

TROPICAL COOLER

1 cup unsweetened pineapple juice

10 medium-sized strawberries, either frozen (without sugar) or fresh

1 small scoop lemon sherbet, or Lemon-Orange Italian Ice from page 65, or Banana Smash from page 103

You will need:
blender

1. Put all the ingredients into the container of a blender. Put the cover of the blender on tightly.

2. Run the machine until everything is well mixed and slushy.

Makes 1 big drink.

CHAPTER 16

POINTERS
FROM
PABLO

THE two detectives were throwing a football in front of Encyclopedia's house when Pablo Pizarro, Idaville's greatest boy artist, stopped to watch.

"No cook should ignore the appearance of food," Pablo said out of nowhere.

Sally's eyes widened at the sight of him, and she fumbled an easy catch. "Hi," she breathed.

Encyclopedia never liked the way Sally mooned over Pablo. So he went directly to the point. "You've heard."

"Heard what?" Pablo asked innocently.

"Sally told the gang during the touch football game Friday that we were going to bake chocolate chip cookies today."

"Why, yes," Pablo admitted carelessly. "But I'd forgotten. I came by merely to help you and Sally."

"How thoughtful of you!" cried Sally. "I'm sure you can give us a real artist's view of cooking!"

"Naturally," Pablo said. "Artists have always been interested in the color, texture, and shape of food. Take van Gogh and Cézanne, to name only two. They were inspired by simple fruits and vegetables. They painted potatoes, carrots, apples, and watermelons."

Sally clapped her hands in delight. "Oh, Pablo, you know so much. You're full of things that aren't even in cookbooks!"

"Like sweet talk," Encyclopedia thought in disgust.

"The look of food is terribly important," Pablo went on. He was gazing softly at Sally, and he spoke as if Encyclopedia weren't there. "You must never forget how food is presented—how it is served has as much to do with cooking as does eating."

"I never thought of that," exclaimed Sally. "I want to hear more. Would you like some chocolate chip cookies? We took them out of the oven only half an hour ago."

Pablo shrugged. "If you insist."

As Sally led him into the house, Pablo mouthed on. "Serve hot food on hot dishes," he said, "and cold food on chilled dishes."

Encyclopedia managed not to kick him in the seat of his pants.

Sally lifted the cookies from the baking tin. She apologized for how they were served—on a paper plate covered with wax paper.

Pablo's smile was forgiving. "Sometimes the server is more important than the manner of serving," he said.

Sally blushed. Encyclopedia ground his teeth.

"I'll try just one," Pablo said.

Encyclopedia watched him eat seven in three minutes.

Before Pablo could reach for the eighth, Encyclopedia

was steering him toward the front door. On the way out, Pablo recited: "We may live without friends. We may live without books. But civilized man cannot live without cooks."

Encyclopedia closed the door after him, hard.

Sally frowned her disapproval. "You were downright rude. You all but threw him out."

"He got to me," Encyclopedia replied. "Why couldn't he come out and say he wanted some cookies instead of pitching all that arty stuff at us?"

"Oh, it's no use arguing," Sally said. "Let's forget it. Cooking is too much fun to be spoiled by anything so silly."

Encyclopedia agreed. "We can always bake more cookies," he said. "Maybe next time we'll *invite* Pablo."

Then he smiled at his thought. The Brown Detective Agency was closed for the winter, but the Brown kitchen was open all year round.

THE Tigers knew that if you eat parsley, it will take away bad breath, even the smell of garlic.

But they forgot they had eaten with their hands.

Unfortunately for them, Encyclopedia was on the case. He told Sally to sniff the hands of each Tiger.

"Garlic," she said over and over as she went from Bugs to Duke to Spike to Rocky. "Yuk!"

"You Tigers nearly got away with it," said Encyclopedia. "If you had washed your hands with strong soap, the garlic smell would have disappeared."

Sally laughed. "The Tigers wash their hands? Never!"

Trapped by their own mistake, the Tigers all chipped in enough money to pay Josh back for the ingredients for chocolate cake and garlic bread.

THE CASE OF THE FOURTH OF JULY ARTIST

THE Liberty Bell didn't crack until 1835. That was long after Nathaniel Tarbox Wiggins died. If he had seen the bell on July 4, 1776, or any other day of his life, he would have seen the bell without a crack.

When Encyclopedia pointed out this fact, the crowd of children lost interest in the raffle.

As Wilford was sadly folding his stepladder, Sally approached him. "That picture isn't half bad," she said. "Did you paint it yourself?"

"All by myself," Wilford replied. "It took me weeks to paint it and to rub it with dirt and give it lots of coats of dark shellac to make it look old."

The crowd of children and the parade were finished for the day. So was Wilford.

THE CASE OF THE OVEN MITT

Feinfinger's
KitchenWare
← DELIVERIES

AT the party, Encyclopedia had asked Hermes, "Did you get your mother's gift?"

Since it was Hermes's birthday, anyone hearing the question should have thought Encyclopedia meant: Did you get the gift from your mother?

But Nancy Frumm said, "Yes, what did you get her?" That is, *for her.*

So Nancy knew Hermes had bought his mother a gift, and not the other way around. She could only have known this by overhearing Hermes talking with Bella and the detectives *while she was in the storeroom.*

Her slip of the tongue did not slip past Encyclopedia.

Nancy confessed. She had been biking down the alley when she saw the storeroom door ajar. She had sneaked in and stolen the two mixers.

THE CASE OF THE OVERSTUFFED PIÑATA

IN Hector's Department Store, Encyclopedia had seen three piñatas fall off the counter. The clay jar broke. But the two papier-mâché bulls bounced. Had they been filled with candy, they would have been too heavy to bounce.

When Bugs claimed he had bought the piñata bull at Hector's, Encyclopedia got him to say he had just bought it "a few minutes ago." Therefore, it should still have been *empty!*

But Tim's aunt had stuffed it with a lot of candy. The number of stamps on the wrapping paper showed that the package had weighed more than a papier-mâché bull would weigh by itself.

Encyclopedia challenged Bugs to go to the store and weigh the piñata bull. Knowing it was full and heavy, Bugs refused.

But he gave Tim back the bull.

WHEN Candida's father learned from Encyclopedia who had stolen Christopher Columbus Day, he went directly to the state park.

The two men who had been roasting a "chicken" admitted stealing and eating the goose. Rather than have trouble with the police, they paid Candida's father far more than a goose is worth.

Encyclopedia nearly missed the clue—till Candida mentioned the tall woman's "dark brown shirt." The word "dark" triggered his memory. He realized the two men had lied. They'd been eating a goose, not a chicken.

A goose has only dark meat. The slice the men had cut off the breast and given Encyclopedia was *dark*. Had it really been from a chicken's breast, the meat would have been *white*.

THE CASE OF THE SECRET RECIPE

FLO was the thief.

She had gone to Beauford's house twenty minutes early and looked into the kitchen window. When she saw that he was busy making French fries, she had sneaked into the museum by the back door.

After stealing the potato with the autographs and substituting an ordinary one, she had returned to the house shortly before noon for the tasting.

She confessed when Encyclopedia pointed out her mistake—the bottle of ketchup.

She would not have brought ketchup to the table unless she knew that Beauford's Tubers a la Twitty was not some fancy dish but simply French fries.

THE CASE OF THE CHINESE RESTAURANT

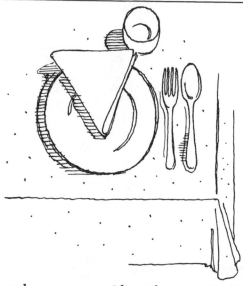

KATE wanted revenge on Oliver because he had beaten her in the election for treasurer of the Service Club.

So she got Mitch to help her steal the money belonging to the Lettermen's Club while Oliver was in the washroom. Then they blamed Oliver.

Encyclopedia saw through their story immediately. Oliver could not have opened the envelope "with a table knife."

In Chinese restaurants, knives are not part of the table setting. They are brought to the table only after the customer has ordered a steak or something that requires a knife to cut.

And Oliver had not yet ordered. As Mitch himself stated, the waiter was just bringing Oliver a menu when he and Kate sat down!

DONALD J. SOBOL has written sixty books for young readers, including more than twenty-five about Encyclopedia Brown. Among his numerous awards, he received a special Edgar Allan Poe Award from the Mystery Writers of America for his contribution to mystery writing.

Mr. Sobol was born in New York City and attended Oberlin College in Oberlin, Ohio. He lives in Miami, Florida, with his wife.